Noah's Schizophrenia

A Mother's Search for Truth

Published by Lisa Hagan Books 2020

www.lisahaganbooks.com

Twitter @LisaHaganBooks

Instagram: LisaHaganBooks

Facebook: LisaHaganBooks

Cover and Interior layout by Simon Hartshorne

Noah's Schizophrenia

A Mother's Search for Truth

KARTAR DIAMOND

Science offers approaches to spectrum psychotic disorders that make them manageable; every person with serious mental illness deserves that care. Diamond's journey with her son is, unfortunately, more of the norm than the exception. The more we speak about this injustice the more likely will we be able to change the status quo. **–Dr. Robert S. Laitman**, Co-Author of *Clozapine: Meaningful Recovery from Schizophrenia*

Kartar Diamond's memoir, **Noah's Schizophrenia**:*A Mother's Search for Truth,* gives constructive descriptions of the experiences many parents have as they struggle to cope with a loved one whose life has been undermined and marginalized by schizophrenia. This book is so helpful to family members who face similar problems finding appropriate treatment and residential care for a mentally ill person. **–Robert Paul Liberman, M.D.,** Distinguished Professor of Psychiatry, UCLA School of Medicine

CONTENTS

Dedication

To all family members and the loved ones of
those who live with schizophrenia.

To all the souls who work tirelessly, without accolades,
to serve and protect the most needy and vulnerable.

To the brave individuals who are mentally interesting
and march to the beat of their own drum.

Introduction

When my son's mental illness first emerged, we visited a series of doctors and therapists who had questions for me since he was a minor and they valued my input. Among the questions, they wanted to know if we had any history of mental illness in our family. Even though I had referred to my mother many times as a neurotic Jewish housewife, I had no awareness of any serious mental illness within the family tree.

I also referred to myself as a "melancholy optimist" because of the way I viewed the world and how I experienced life a little differently than those around me. I always tried to keep my existentialist despair at bay by seeking out humor and the beauty of nature all around. As a young person, I also found a way to channel my emotions into lyric writing; that felt less "indulgent" to me than seeking therapy.

Mental health professionals asked if I had a normal pregnancy, which I did, and perhaps better than normal. I only had mild morning sickness in the first trimester, gained only twenty-four pounds, and delivered my son naturally, weighing in at 7.7 pounds. I was happier than ever to become a mother and my migraines disappeared completely. At least the doctors were looking for a genetic or gestational cause for my son's schizophrenia, unlike decades ago, when it was blamed on bad parenting.

Noah also developed better than normal; he sat up, crawled, walked, and talked, all ahead of schedule. Because I refused to talk "baby talk" with him, he developed a large vocabulary and an understanding of sentence structure very early on. He was breastfed for twenty months and as a kid, he enjoyed eating vegetables daily. Perhaps that is why he rarely got sick. He may have had only one or two mild colds up until the age of fourteen.

That year, he contracted whooping cough, even though he had the vaccine for it as a younger child. Years later I would wonder if his getting whooping cough had anything to do with a mandatory second round of vaccines required just before he entered a private high school. In retrospect, that was the very beginning of his personality change.

Like other parents, we go back in time searching for any clues as to why a mental illness emerged. Knowing there is a movement of parents who attribute their child's autism to vaccines, I couldn't help but wonder if there was any link to his mental illness, set in motion by either the second round of vaccines or whooping cough itself. I later learned that even though schizophrenia usually starts in the late teens or early twenties, there is such a distinction as Early Onset Schizophrenia, which starts even younger and might be triggered just by puberty.

If I had not been forced to learn about schizophrenia and all the serious side effects of the medications used for it, I would be like most people. I would either know next to nothing or I would hold some misconceptions about it, still common to this day. Just as a couple of examples, many people think that a person with schizophrenia suffers from "madness" and they are out of touch with reality on a perpetual basis. Many people also expect that a person who faithfully takes their medication can resume a normal life and functionality. Neither of these assumptions is true or true all the time; the misinformation and downright discrimination continue.

We are living in "interesting times" as the Chinese curse implies. While we go the extra mile to accommodate the transgender community, remodel public bathrooms, and call them by their preferred pronoun, society still makes fun of serious mental illness. Even worse, some still deny its existence. As recently as 2016, the Southern California amusement park Knott's Berry Farm planned a Halloween attraction called VR: 5150. Like a haunted house on steroids, this attraction was supposed to scare people with a ghoulish virtual reality experience of being in a psychiatric ward with zombie-like patients. Fortunately, this grand display of insensitivity and political incorrectness was canceled before it got started when mental health advocates found out about it and protested.

My hope and prayer are that this book will serve as a source of solace for other parents and family members, dealing with this incredible challenge in all our lives. There is comfort in knowing you are not alone. I also hope that some of the mistakes and set-backs our family endured can serve to better guide you and your family to more effective ways of dealing with the deficiencies in the current mental health care system.

For someone who usually has a lot to say, the emotional toll this disease exacts on family members has often left me exhausted and speechless. Family support groups remind us that we are members of a "club" we don't want to be in, but we find hope and camaraderie grieving with each other. It should be noted that even though I refer to the struggles of parents throughout this memoir, other family members experience their traumas, such as siblings. Many siblings suffer from "survivor's guilt" or under-standably resent all the time their parents spent focusing on their brother or sister with problems.

I hope any family member or caretaker can glean from this memoir what they need to improve their unique situation. This club also gives birth to new friendships, which we welcome since other older friendships sometimes end because of the stigma. Well-meaning friends often find themselves at a loss in how to help or comfort us, so they quietly slip away.

Our mentally ill loved one had goals and ambitions for their own life which may never be realized. Our hopes and dreams for them have been crushed as well. We feel bitter about the mistakes we made, how we handled the most frightening situations, and we quietly try to keep our resentment at bay for the portions of our own lives ruined by the trauma of trying to help someone who often does not want our help.

I also hope this book is read by those working in the mental health care system, in any capacity. This memoir is for those who want to better understand the frustrations and the perspective of family members with a loved one who has schizophrenia. I may not mention bipolar disorder or other seriously debilitating diagnoses, as the emphasis is on schizophrenia, but you can "fill in the blank" where it addresses your situation. Family members are usually one of the most important assets, to be included in every step of the way in the recovery process for the mentally ill individual. Family members are sometimes dismissed as part of the problem and not included in vital decisions when they can assist in irreplaceable ways.

Finally, I do hope that books like mine get into the hands of legislators and policy-makers. There is an innocent human face on this tragedy and the way we deal with it needs a complete overhaul. Long term, comprehensive and well-funded solutions need to be implemented, instead of misdirected knee-jerk reactions to the next mass shooting or other atrocities caused by *un*treated mental illness.

We should not *just* be protecting those with untreated mental illness from causing harm or to reduce their misery. We should also encourage the natural talent and aptitude of those with schizophrenia. They are so often intellectually and artistically gifted, that it is a cliché. Some of the greatest individuals to walk this Earth, like Nikola Tesla, Vincent Van Gogh, Jack Kerouac, Buddy Bolen, (often credited as the founder of Jazz,) and Nobel-prizewinning mathematician John Nash, made enormous contributions to the world, despite their afflictions. No doubt, humanity benefits if we could relieve the suffering of these misunderstood geniuses. When they are allowed to fulfill their creative and intellectual gifts, the world can be a better place for all.

ONE:

Can Someone Tell Me
What Is Going On?

My son stood in the living room, his hands over his head, anguish in his eyes, screaming "Every musician in L.A. is stealing my ideas!" I was blown away by what he said. I couldn't understand why he would make such a statement. I could tell he was upset and dead serious, so I tried to comfort him by being rational. I responded to Noah by saying "But you don't even know every musician in L.A., so how could that be possible?"

He was only fifteen years old, and already he was an excellent musician who played in a couple of bands with schoolmates. At age eleven he formed his group called the Liquid Nixons. His delusion that adult musicians in Los Angeles were stealing his ideas seemed to come out of nowhere. Years later, I would learn that when a person is in a psychotic state, trying to be rational with the person, or refuting their reality, is just going to make things worse. Allowing the person to know you think their perceptions may not be grounded in reality is not a way to garner trust or de-escalate a crisis.

Up until that point, my communication with my son had always been enjoyable and sympathetic and he even once told me as a youngster that he appreciated the way I explained things to him. Not now. I couldn't comfort him at all and he stomped off into his bedroom.

Every ten minutes that same night, Noah came out of his bedroom, which was right next to my home office, and popped his head into the room. With a glassy look in his big brown eyes and a crazed smile on his young handsome face, he announced which rock star he had just become. I didn't know whether he was joking or not. He went back into his room, turned up the music, listened to a couple of songs from Ziggy Stardust, and then came into my office to say, "Now I am David Bowie!" Minutes later, after listening to some other musical icon, he again barged in on me and stated he had become this person or that person. It was a total departure from his usual behavior.

Noah already owned the image of a teen idol. At 5' 6" with a lean frame, his thick shoulder-length brown hair made him look like a young Jimmy Page or Harry Styles. Later in the evening, he emerged from his bedroom just wearing his boxer shorts. He went into the living room and started whipping the couch with a belt, laughing manically! After a while, he quieted down, retreated to his bedroom for the rest of the evening and I was left confused and worried.

I made a phone call to his father. In retrospect, if I had understood then what I know today, I would have taken him to the hospital immediately. Of course, there was no second-guessing whether or not he would have gone with me willingly. But the next day he did. We went to the Emergency Room. There were no other people besides us in the Reception area, so I had no reason to anticipate much of a wait. For almost three hours, we were mostly ignored, except for bringing my son into a small exam room to get his insurance information and to get weighed.

Every thirty minutes or so, some staff person came and lied to us about how he would be seen momentarily. Noah and I were both getting hungry and hypoglycemic. After the fourth time they tried to stall, we just left. Little did I know then, waiting for emergency psychiatric treatment can take not only hours but sometimes even days! It would be nine years later that my son waited FIVE days in the ER at another hospital before being admitted.

To add insult to injury, a few weeks later I got a bill from the hospital ER for several hundred dollars. I called the ER and told them, using some choice words, that no services were provided and that if they continued to try to collect a fee for no services rendered, I would report them to the State for insurance fraud. That was just the first of many frustrating episodes with hospitals and insurance companies, trying to pull a fast one at my son's expense.

Noah's mental breakdown in our living room that night was a culmination of increasingly bizarre behaviors spanning some months before. About six months before our aborted visit to the Emergency Room, he and I had gone out to dinner. After our meal, Noah decided to do what many teenagers do, which is walk about a half-block ahead of their parents, so as not to be seen or associated with said parent. This is typical teenage behavior, which I found amusing, but not that night. Noah continued to walk past the parking structure where the car was parked. I stopped and waited to see how long he would continue walking, without looking back at me.

A block later, he finally stopped, looked back at me, and I motioned with my hand that I intended to turn left into the parking structure. I then waited for him to walk back to me. Noah was visibly annoyed. When he joined me where I waited, Noah said he didn't like the way I waved my hand. He said it was disrespectful. I chose to ignore the comment because I thought he was just being a cranky teenager, although I had to admit to myself this was a departure from his normal courteous, affection-ate, and mellow demeanor. This was the same teenager who used to refer to himself as my "mini-me" when he was younger. He saw the commercials on TV for the *Austin Powers* movie, with the character played by Verne Troyer. He once coyly said to me, "I'm your Mini-Me....You complete me!" And he did. We were buddies, but not that night.

When we got home, Noah promptly sat down at the kitchen table, put his head down, and started crying! I asked him what was wrong and he said, "I know you *care* about me, but you don't *love* me!" Now, compared to his comment about not liking the way I waved my hand, this statement was really strange. I asked him why he thinks I didn't love him and Noah struggled to be as tactful as he was distraught. He said slowly, "You don't *understand* me, so you can't *love* me." At this point, I had to admit I didn't understand him or where this surge of emotional outburst came from. So, I reacted with what I thought would be a less charged response. I told him it's possible to love someone you don't understand and how that, in and of itself, was a good example of *un*conditional love. He didn't buy it. He wanted to make it clear to me I no longer understood him, and by definition, didn't love him.

This was close to the summer of 2006, when just a few bread crumbs were dropped, a trail leading up to the couch whipping incident six months later. Noah's personality was changing, not in a good way, as if a different person possessed him. One day, within earshot of Noah, I called his father who I had divorced more than ten years prior. We had a 50/50 joint custody schedule, one week on and one week off. It never vacillated. If I had to go out of town, I did it in the week when I didn't have Noah; I could focus on him when he was at my house. I got used to the schedule eventually, but in the beginning, it was rough. On the weeks when I didn't have my little boy with me, it felt wrong. My house seemed empty.

I couldn't help but feel that only having my son with me every other week went against nature. A little boy should be with his mother every day. But in the imperfect world of custody arrangements, we split our child evenly, if not in half. I told myself it made more sense for him to be with me full time until he was a teenager, but I wasn't given that option. Still, I looked forward to the day when he could make his own choice regarding which parent to live with.

We had such a strong bond that I fantasized about him living just with me in the future while going to college locally at UCLA or USC. I would have also been the kind of mom to let my adult son live at home, helping him save money while pursuing his career in music. He could have turned the den into a recording studio and I would have continued to be in awe of the amazing guitar riffs I was blessed to hear traveling throughout the house. When Noah was much older, I didn't have the heart to tell him that one of his childhood friends, with unimpressive musical skills as a teen, became a working musician who toured the world.

Back to reality, my only consolation with the joint custody schedule was that on the weeks when he was not with me, I knew he was in good hands, with a very attentive step-mom who I liked a lot. At times, however, I cringed, hearing my six year old refer to his father and step-mom as "his parents." Were it not for the awkwardness of having been married to the same man, she and I probably could have been good friends. Step-mom #1 lasted for seven years and then Step-mom #2 took her place when Noah was about thirteen. Stepmom #2 moved in only six months after Step-Mom #1 moved out. That was a shock to Noah, for sure. But a year later, he warmed up to her.

"How are things going over at your house?" Without missing a beat, Noah's father replied over the phone, "Oh, is he psycho-analyzing you as well?" We laughed. His dad then said, "Yeah, I was thinking about buying him that book, *Psychology for Dummies*, so that he might know what he's talking about." At that moment, I think we both chalked it up to teenage hormones and we were not concerned, just yet.

TWO:

The First of Many Mistakes

In the summer of 2006, when Noah was fifteen, I suggested we go on a little road trip. I found out there was a festival going on in San Francisco's Haight-Ashbury district and Noah loved anything to do with the 1960's music and hippies. He was up for the road trip I planned and we drove straight to Monterey, the first leg of the journey, arriving in San Francisco on Day Two. Once we got to Haight-Ashbury, Noah wanted to walk around by himself. We were at one end of the festival, with booths, food, tie-died T-shirts, love beads, and music all around. His mood had turned a little somber and I wanted him to feel like he was his own man, so I agreed to go separate ways and to meet up again in one hour.

Later that night, as we were finishing having dinner, I started to pay the bill and asked Noah if he knew how to figure out 20% of a dinner bill. On my mind was the thought it wouldn't be long before he would be going out with friends, sans parents. I wanted him to know it is customary to leave a 20% tip for decent service. Our bill was $35.00. I asked him if he knew what 20% of $35.00 was and he looked at me as if I asked him what the composition of dirt was on the moon.

He was annoyed and said he couldn't figure that out. This surprised me because my kid had always gotten A's in math. I didn't want him to feel like I was judging him, but I was genuinely surprised. I walked it back a little and said to him that even I can't figure everything out in my head, but my process for determining a tip is to take 10% of the bill and then double it.

This still mystified him. I asked Noah if he knew what 10% of $35.00 was. He said he didn't know. I told him it was $3.50 and you just moved a decimal point, then doubled that amount to get to 20%. Noah asked me if I had a pen. I gave him one out of my purse and he grabbed a napkin. He started drawing circles on the napkin and then gave up.

I asked Noah what he was doing and he said he needed to draw out thirty-five circles and then group them to figure out what this elusive 20% was. He was pissed off and I didn't want to argue with him in the restaurant, so I told him to let it go. At this point, my heart sank. I knew something was wrong. Had he gotten stoned during that hour we spent apart from each other? What the hell was going on?

The rest of our time in San Francisco was pleasant but subdued. We stayed one night at a famous old Victorian hotel and went on a Haunted House walking tour. We went to a few other classic tourist traps and then headed back to L.A. Further into the summer, I suggested we go on another short trip, this time to Seattle, home to one of his favorite rock stars, Kurt Cobain of Nirvana. Noah was excited about going and I tried to make it as much fun as possible for a fifteen-year-old with his mom. Being from L.A., I just assumed that there would be some kind of Dead Celebrity Tour bus to take us by Kurt Cobain's last residence in Seattle, but they had no such thing available. Instead, we went to the Space Needle, a Rock Music Museum, Pike's Place, and we stumbled upon a bronze statue of Jimi Hendrix, another one of my son's favorite guitar players.

As the summer of 2006 came to a close, Noah announced he wanted to live with his father instead of half time with each of us. I was initially surprised because Noah and I had always been so close and got along so well. There were numerous times when he was little, Noah would beg to live just with me, but I always told him his father wanted as much time with him as I did. We had had some problems in our divorce and in co-parenting, but much of that tension was behind us now and it occurred to me maybe it would be good for Noah to spend more time with his dad. Especially with the teenage hormones flowing, perhaps there was something to be gained with him getting more male energy and guidance in his life. Our households were only ten minutes apart; it wasn't like I couldn't still see Noah as often as I wanted. I agreed to abandon the 50/50 custody schedule.

In less than twenty-four hours, I found out the real reason why Noah wanted to move over to his dad's house full-time. He had been offered the opportunity to live in the detached guesthouse and not in the bedroom he had inside the main house. Well, if I were a fifteen-year-old boy, I would want to have my own "pad" too! I called his father and left a voicemail message. I said, "Watch him like a hawk; if I were a teenage boy with my own guesthouse, I would be smoking pot, staying up all night, and sneaking girls over, so please pay attention!" That is exactly what happened, although we found out later that the pot-smoking began much earlier before Noah moved into the guesthouse at his dad's. Eventually, the report card came in, showing Noah had missed many of his first Period classes, despite being dropped off at school early. Little did I know he snuck off campus after arriving at school, to smoke pot and God-knows-what else. A real addiction had developed right under our noses. Once I knew my son was turning into a musician, I almost assumed we might end up dealing with drug issues somewhere down the line when he was older. Had I known drug use in early adolescence can be evidence of self-medicating from the symptoms of an emerging brain disorder, I would never let him out of my sight!

Years earlier, when Noah was not more than about twelve or thirteen, he made me aware his school had drug prevention presentations. I told him when I was a teenager in the 1970s, kids smoked a whole bag of marijuana to get high. He seemed to already know marijuana had become much stronger and just one hit off a joint could do the job of a whole bag of pot from decades past.

Noah then told me he asked all his friends' parents if they had taken drugs in the '60s. I couldn't believe he was polling all these adults and not one of them called to tell me. I asked Noah what his poll revealed to him. He told me they had all tried psychedelics and taken drugs at rock concerts, but admonished him not to do it! Noah was trying to reconcile the warnings from the anti-drug campaign going on at his school, with the wild, glamorous hippie stories told to him by his friends' parents. I said to him, "and they all lived to tell, right?" and he said, "Right." At that point, I knew he had satisfied his curiosity about the dangers of taking drugs. None of them died, so he would not be taking the "Just Say No" rhetoric seriously.

Within three weeks of living only at his dad's, I got a phone call from panicky step-mom #2. This was about two months before I witnessed with my own eyes Noah's meltdown when he "became" David Bowie. She was concerned because Noah said all kinds of bizarre and paranoid things. Like what? She said he wanted to go to India to "be with his people," he was a "genius" and only his people in India understood him. Noah also claimed the neighbor, who he didn't know, tried to steal all his ideas. He also said his father was putting "sexual energy" into the food and that was why he couldn't eat at their house. This was more than raging teenage hormones. This might not even just be drug-induced delusions. I told her we needed to get him to a therapist immediately and I started to look up psychologists in the area, who were covered under his insurance plan. This was the beginning of many mistakes made in dealing with Noah, his turmoil, and his emerging mental illness.

In a snap decision, we decided to have Noah see a friend of his father, who was a therapist, but adolescents were not his area of expertise. Still, we thought to start with Dr. Greenberg because he knew Noah from the time he was a baby and we didn't yet even understand the scope of what was happening. In retrospect, this therapist was way out of his league. He should have recommended us right away to a specialist in adolescent psychiatry. Instead, we wasted nearly a year with Dr. Greenberg. After only a few sessions with him and no diagnosis, Dr. Greenberg alluded to the probability that we may have to take Noah to the hospital if his paranoia and delusions continue. Never having done this before, I asked Dr. Greenberg what we should do or say to the doctors when we get to the hospital. Trying to be funny, Dr. Greenberg told me to just announce "we're Jewish."

Weeks later, we did end up at the hospital, but we didn't announce that we were Jewish or ate chopped liver. Our first episode at the hospital lasted three hours; no one saw us so we left. I soon suspected we needed a second opinion, so I found an adolescent psychiatrist who pronounced Noah as schizophrenic on the first visit and prescribed Abilify. Only a month later, Dr. Porter downgraded Noah's diagnosis to "social anxiety," based on feedback from Noah directly. To my surprise, Dr. Porter recommended Noah discontinue the medication. If I knew back then that a sudden termination in medication could trigger another psychotic break, I would have insisted Noah taper off slowly. Tapering off medication is called "titration" or "titrating" and it is critical to avoid serious relapse. Removing medications takes careful calibration to avoid serious physical harm as well; such as heart attack or stroke. It's serious business.

I asked Noah if he could let me know what he discussed with Dr. Porter in the few sessions he had with him. Noah only told me he was suffering from gynecomastia (the enlargement of male breast tissue) and he wanted me to schedule breast reduction surgery for him. I asked Noah to lift his shirt so I could see for myself if he was developing breasts. Barely sixteen years old, Noah was a lean guy and flat as a board in his chest area. More delusions for Noah; more panic for me. I researched the term "body dysmorphia." Noah's father had a cousin who was anorexic as a teenager; that is a sustained delusion. Was there a connection?

Noah stopped seeing Dr. Porter after only a half dozen sessions and we naively continued to seek counsel with Dr. Greenberg. I didn't think twice about terminating the sessions with Dr. Porter. How could a diagnosis of schizophrenia turn into Social Anxiety a month later? How could a psychiatrist not recognize that body dysmorphia is a sustained delusion and not the same as anxiety?

We continued to let Noah see Dr. Greenberg on a weekly basis for another couple of months, but no diagnosis came and there was no improvement in Noah's behavior. He did not act normal in any way and I was partially out of the loop because Noah continued to live in the guesthouse at his dad's. One night when I took Noah out to dinner, he told me he had gone a full week without sleeping. He seemed amused and almost proud of accomplishing such a feat.

Dr. Greenberg hinted that if Noah didn't improve under his care, one option would be to send him away to a therapeutic residential school out of state. I did not know these places existed, but it seemed quite extreme at the time. In response, I suggested we increase the therapy sessions from once per week with just Noah and Dr. Greenberg to include once per week as a family, and a third weekly session with just me and Noah's father to discuss our son without Noah being there. Dr. Greenberg already told us how expensive the out-of-state residential school would be, so I figured we should first try something more comprehensive amongst ourselves. All agreed this was a good approach before choosing something as extreme as shipping our son off to a residential school we knew nothing about. Unfortunately, shortly after beginning these three-times-per week sessions with Dr. Greenberg, he seemed more interested in his own witty asides than our son's undiagnosed behaviors.

Dr. Greenberg also seemed to take great delight in dredging up old wounds from our divorce and pitting me against my ex-husband. Here we were, focusing on our son, and being very much "on the same page," yet Dr. Greenberg tried to stir up old issues. I guess, in retrospect, since he really had no idea how to handle our son, he thought he would just persist with post-marriage family counseling. I even brought it up to my ex-husband more than once; who agreed how odd it was that Dr. Greenberg was haranguing us, as a former couple, when he should concentrate on Noah.

Some of the family sessions bordered on total lunacy. One time, Dr. Greenberg told us that in the previous session, Noah confided in him about his extensive drug use. Noah smoked pot and took psychedelics. He also tried cocaine and alcohol. He told Dr. Greenberg he was *not* just taking drugs for recreational reasons, but for spiritual research. Regardless of my son's motives, Dr. Greenberg seemed to support the "spiritual research" and even mentioned that one could major in "consciousness" at the University of Colorado!

Dr. Greenberg didn't seem to be giving our son any sage advice about *not* doing drugs, but rather quite the opposite. I looked at Dr. Greenberg, who had a ten-year-old son at the time. I said to him, "So, if your son starts experimenting with drugs six years from now in the name of spiritual research, are you going to be perfectly fine with that?" Dr. Greenberg really didn't like me for a variety of reasons, not the least of which was that I called him on his bullshit. He could not give me a straight answer about whether he would apply the same support to his own son if he discovered he did drugs.

After a few months, I could see our family therapy was not going anywhere. Sessions with him seemed more like a Seinfeld episode where we were just supposed to laugh at his jokes. It became obvious to me he felt Noah's dad and I were horrible parents and he needed to cozy up to Noah, garner his trust, and pretend to be some kind of surrogate father figure.

Dr. Greenberg was so out of touch with our son's serious mental illness he suggested we should send him away in the approaching summer of 2007, to teach English as a second language in Japan! He told us how life-affirming his own experience was when he went to Switzerland for a summer in his teens. At this point, I told Dr. Greenberg that if Noah wanted to continue to see him, I would permit it, but I had to bow out of these ludicrous unhelpful family therapy sessions.

How on Earth was my son going to go to a foreign country and teach English to Japanese students when he was too paranoid to attend his own high school? Just months before, we had to find a small private school for Noah when he refused to go to his regular public high school for fear that the Crips and the Bloods were going to kill him. I even called to find out if there was any real concern about gang activity at his high school in West Los Angeles. I was promptly told "no."

Noah shaved his head bald around this time, hung out with some kid who was supplying the drugs and stayed awake in the guesthouse for days at a time. But this clueless therapist thought Noah might "snap out of it" by spending a summer teaching in Japan. Juxtapose this hair-brained idea with the seriousness of having previously suggested Noah be sent to an out-of-state school for troubled teens and you have an idea of the clueless behavior of this doctor!

As Dr. Greenberg tried to arrange with my ex-husband for our son to stay with someone in Japan, Noah had a full-blown psychotic breakdown in New Mexico. His father had driven the two of them to New Mexico for a meditation retreat. My son never liked these events but felt he had to go on an annual basis, regardless. I learned later, that halfway there, Noah was acting strangely in a hotel room in Arizona, taking a shower with his clothes on. Instead of turning around and coming back to Los Angeles for emergency care, they pressed on to New Mexico. Once at the retreat, a rather rugged camping site, Noah continued to decompensate to the point where he was rolling around in the dirt. An ambulance was called and he was taken to a nearby hospital. Noah was wild with mania, highly agitated, and spitting at the hospital staff.

This little hospital in a small town decided they couldn't handle him safely, so he was sent days later to a major hospital in Albuquerque. The following week I had an exasperating exchange on the phone with our health insurance company. They disputed the ambulance fee since we didn't call them in advance to get authorization, as if people have the presence of mind to call their insurance in the middle of a crisis! Noah stayed for eight days in this larger hospital's adolescent psychiatric ward. Horrible as it was, it was better he was there than alone in Japan! Thank God that ridiculous scheme never came to pass.

At the first hospital in the little town, the treating doctor there gave Noah a diagnosis: schizoaffective disorder. We learned quickly that this meant schizophrenia with an additional mood disorder. Later that summer, another hospitalization yielded a different diagnosis: bipolar disorder with psychotic features. Bipolar disorder describes an illness from mild to severe, where a person's moods vacillate from depression on one end to mania on the other. Bipolar Disorder used to be called "Manic Depression" when my own mother was labeled with it in the 1940s.

Mania, whether it is part of bipolar disorder or schizophrenia, can start out with the person being full of energy, ideas, and even some very productive and creative outcomes. But there is an arc to the mania where the euphoria and energy wear off and agitation sets in. Left untreated, the mania can transform into full-blown psychosis. This can also lead to some very risky, dangerous behaviors, threats to others, and self-harm. Weeks later, after Noah's breakdown in New Mexico, I asked him if he could describe to me what he was feeling during that time. He didn't want to talk much, but managed to tell me that when he was in the mountains of New Mexico he could "see and hear everything around him for miles." Delusions of grandeur are also symptoms of bipolar disorder and schizophrenia.

Even though bipolar disorder proved later to be an incorrect diagnosis for Noah, the diagnosis stuck for a while and I began to read books on it. The only consolation in not knowing the correct diagnosis for sure is that many of the same medications are used for either illness. He has been on so many different medications, I've lost track of the exact timeline for each. But I believe he was put on Depakote initially, which is one of many medications used to treat bipolar disorder or schizophrenia when anxiety is present. It can also be prescribed at a much smaller dose for depression. (Depakote has a long history treating epilepsy and seizure disorders.)

Schizophrenia is not one, but a cluster or spectrum of disorders. I've even read some researchers believe it may be on the Autism spectrum. To quote Dr. Robert S. Laitman, co-author of *Clozapine: A Meaningful Recovery from Schizophrenia*, whose son has schizophrenia, and who shared with me some of his presentation papers, "Schizophrenia spectrum disorders are heterogeneous neurologic syndromes that derive from a complex interplay of inheritance, aberrant neurodevelopment, and environmental triggers." This means there is a genetic predisposition, and then either environmental stresses bring it out of dormancy and/or it is caused by a departure in normal brain development, often around puberty.

Dr. Laitman went on, "The clinical definition continues to state that the following symptoms must be present for over a month's duration and one of the symptoms must be either a delusion, hallucinations, or disorganized speech. The other two defining characteristics are catatonia or disorganized behavior or negative symptoms such as: lack of motivation, diminished emotional expression, along with impairment in major areas of functioning; such as work, school, interpersonal relations, and self-care. This combination of symptoms must last for at least six months."

Occasionally, people experience symptoms that present like schizophrenia, but turn out not to be. Author and neurologist Dr. Oliver Sacks wrote a book titled *Hallucinations,* which discusses all kinds of non-permanent medical conditions that can cause a person to temporarily hallucinate. About two years into Noah's illness, his father arranged for a brain scan, to rule out a tumor. What was discovered on the scan were "enlarged ventricles." This is one of the few physical signs of possible schizophrenia, gaps in gray mater. When parents are forewarned of what to look for in an emerging mental illness or drug use, a sudden change in personality, relationships, performance in school, and sleeping and eating habits can also be indicators.

The hospital in Albuquerque discharged Noah eight days later and once back at his dad's house in Los Angeles it became evident that he was not at all stable. Noah somehow got ahold of his stepmom's journal and didn't like whatever she wrote about him or the current events. He became aggressive with her and she immediately left town to stay for a while with her adult daughter.

We called a local hospital covered under Noah's insurance plan, only to find out that they had no beds available. The hospital literally asked me to call daily to find out if they had any openings and at some point weeks later they did. This is where Dr. Greenberg tried to commandeer the situation when he should have butted out. He asked us to lie to Noah and tell him that we were just taking him to a doctor for an examination, and not that we were going to be admitting him again to another hospital. This was June of 2007 and we were still letting Noah, now sixteen, see Dr. Greenberg after he returned from New Mexico. Throughout that summer we still consulted with Dr. Greenberg, and in retrospect, that led to more bad decisions.

Once we got Noah to the hospital, they had us wait in the reception room. Dr. Greenberg wanted to get on the phone with Noah and manage the situation, convincing Noah he should just willingly admit himself to the hospital. I understood his good intentions, but trying to execute this plan was like preparing for an underwater birth. While we waited for a doctor to see Noah, he was growing more agitated. He would laugh hysterically one minute and then be brooding the next. If this is what "rapid cycling" bi-polar looked like; we were all witnessing it. Noah couldn't handle waiting to be seen. He threatened to leave and just walk out of the reception room.

It got harder to convince him to stay seated and not keep jumping up and making demands on the hospital staff. At a certain point, he became so disruptive the staff actually gave us an ultimatum: either leave or have him admitted immediately. In other words, there would be no waiting for a doctor to sit down and have a leisurely conversation in his office. I made a quick decision and so I told the staff to admit him. It took weeks to just have the opportunity to walk through their doors. Two strong security guards quickly took Noah, all of his 130 pounds, one on each arm, and escorted him past a set of locked doors. Noah did not look back at either of us. When Dr. Greenberg found out he was furious with me. His plan to convince Noah to admit himself was pre-empted. I made a decision with no time to hesitate as Noah melted right before my eyes.

Noah later became very mad at Dr. Greenberg for tricking him into going to the hospital. Dr. Greenberg blamed me and said their bond of trust (real or imagined) was broken. Noah was at this hospital #3 for a couple of weeks. At first, he was non-compliant and they had to give him the anti-psychotics through injection since he would not take the medication orally. Noah never called from the hospital payphone or asked to see me, but I would visit every few days. The hospital had ridiculously short and inconvenient visiting hours.

Because the patient programs are all scheduled during the day, the visiting hours end up being from around 6 p.m. to 8 p.m. each night. In a place like Southern California, rush hour traffic begins in the afternoon and doesn't end until much later in the evening. Trying to visit a loved one during the dinner hours can mean driving several hours round trip. Family members are not allowed to bring much into the visiting room with them, needing to put their phones and purses into lockers, like we're visiting a jail. By the time one gets through security, the visit with a family member might be painfully brief. There were times when I would drive over two hours, just for a ten to fifteen-minute visit. Sometimes, my only purpose in visiting was to honor Noah's request and bring him some fast food, which tasted better to him than hospital food.

It was during one of these hospital visits, Noah first expressed himself with heightened religiosity, claiming he was reading a Bible he found in his room at the psychiatric ward. I didn't know if he really felt like he was becoming Jesus or if he was just trying to challenge me since he wasn't raised Christian. I later learned that delusions of grandeur and religious themes are extremely common with people suffering from psychoses, as much as the paranoia about being spied on by the government or believing they are in relationships with celebrities.

The psychiatric hospitals must think very highly of the rehabilitation programs they have during the daytime (when no visitors
are allowed). Are they really therapeutic, or do the patients just
attend them so they can get out of the hospital that much sooner
for "good behavior?" Even after Noah was released from this third
hospital stay, he ended up returning just a couple weeks later. He
told one of his friends about the medication he was on and the
friend told him that he would gain a lot of weight on it. Noah
went off those meds immediately. This was back in the naïve days
when we trusted him to take his medications on his own.

Shortly thereafter, he began fighting with his father while
they were driving. Noah punched his father many times in the
arm and a cell phone flew out of the car. Hearing about it from
Noah's step-mom, the fight between Noah and his dad continued
when they got home, wrestling with each other on the front lawn.
Police were called, they did a "5150," and they took Noah straight
back to the same hospital.

With four hospitalizations in two months' time, Dr. Greenberg
pushed hard on the idea of sending Noah away to the therapeutic
school in Utah. The suggestion no longer seemed extreme. Toward
the end of that summer 2007, Dr. Greenberg introduced us to a pair
of social workers, whose sole focus was in arranging for teenagers
to attend these out of state residential schools. The schools were
designed to address mental illness or behavioral problems. It also
became urgent to get Noah away from other teens dabbling in
recreational drugs. A local hospital with a partial day program for
teens had a six-month waiting list; it seemed even clearer Noah
could not get the help he needed locally.

One reason these out-of-state schools exist is that the Age
of Consent in California is only fourteen years old. A child can
literally get a legal separation or emancipation from their own
parents if they have the nerve to demand it. But in several states

like Utah and Texas, a minor can be placed there and then not be able to move because the Age of Consent is eighteen in these states.

We were told by the social workers Noah could not have any knowledge about what was being planned. They told us many kids run away from home if they have any idea they are going to be shipped off somewhere against their will. We made the plans and said nothing to him. It was particularly heart wrenching to finalize the plans because, during those couple weeks, Noah was acting fairly sweet and introspective. Nevertheless, the morning came for him to be woken out of his sleep, at his father's house, by two large men. As parents, we were asked to stay out of his bedroom while the escorts talked to him and explained what was going on. Mom and dad were only able to briefly confirm that this is what we planned and wanted for him and he was going to a place for a little while to get the treatment he needed.

I'm sure Noah was in shock, but there was no yelling or signs of resistance. It all happened very quickly. Shortly after these two hired strangers took Noah to the airport, I saw Noah's father break down and cry as I had never seen before. His father was stoic up until then, but the reality of what just happened must have felt like a gut punch. This ended up being one of the darkest days for Noah's father and me, seeing it all play out, like a SWAT team descending upon our son. He left with just a backpack put together for him and the plan included sending the rest of his clothes by UPS. Without having to go to the airport's baggage claim, the escorts could control our son better, and reduce the chance of him trying to escape or struggle with them at the airport. They needed to hold Noah, not luggage. I apologized to my son numerous times since, not just for sending him away without notice, but for the way he was treated once he was there.

THREE:

Dr. Fake

We had no idea initially how long he would be at the out of state school, which turned out to be nearly two years. Staff felt very confident about their program and said, "Give us six months." Unfortunately, they soon said, less confidently, "Give us one year." I will never know what really went on at the residential school, but their rules establish that a newcomer to the school is at a Level 1 status, and only when they follow the rules do they get to the next level up. At a higher level, a student can leave the campus and go into town with a staff member. Some kids do so well they reach the next higher level and can be trusted to leave the campus on their own. Some kids do so well they can even have occasional home visits, but not Noah. The entire time he was there, for almost two years, he never got past the first level. For all practical purposes, he was in a locked facility.

The School placed Noah in the *Oppositional Defiant Disorder Unit*, even though he entered their program after four hospitalizations and a diagnosis that ranged from bipolar disorder with psychotic features, to paranoid schizophrenia or schizoaffective disorder. That said, Noah was a real anarchist when he arrived there and I heard later he tried to mobilize the other teens into going on a medication strike. In any other context, I would have been proud of Noah for his leadership skills! He was now in the 11th grade and he still got some A's and B's in his classes, but was also highly erratic, even throwing a chair at his teacher once. I sent him a guitar and found out he smashed it sometime shortly after.

I also heard he had a complete meltdown in the school cafeteria because he thought his food was poisoned. I found out later he was under-medicated, and it took a phone call from an outside psychiatrist to convince the staff to increase his dosage.

Dr. Harris was recommended to us, shortly after we sent Noah to the out of state School. He was a specialist in adolescent schizophrenia, so we briefly brought Noah home for the doctor to evaluate. In very little time, Dr. Harris told us that Noah definitely had schizophrenia and not bipolar disorder. We were grateful for his expert skills. Without Noah in the room, Dr. Harris's bedside manner was non-existent. He flatly told Noah's father and me the best medication is Clozapine, but it comes with the highest risks. (I learned years later that this medical concern has been greatly exaggerated. Most people who try Clozapine do well on it.) He also said robotically Noah would probably gain a hundred pounds on Clozapine. I must have looked incredulous at his bluntness, but Dr. Harris followed up with the memorable, "He has a choice. He can be overweight....or insane."

He also said matter-of-factly that Noah would probably spend the rest of his life "in a group home." While we as parents tried to metabolize this dire prognosis, we were still grateful to Dr. Harris for agreeing to call the school in Utah, dialogue with the treating doctor there, and make some additional recommendations. At the time, Noah was on Seroquel and Lamictal and extremely under-medicated, according to Dr. Harris. For him to call, as a non-treating doctor, to make recommendations for an increase in dosage was a risk in professional protocols he was willing to make on our son's behalf. He knew the longer Noah was under-medicated, the worse things would get.

At this school, they had an isolation room that kids would have to go into if they were acting out violently or belligerently. If a teen was in the isolation room, they could not speak to their parents or receive any phone calls. Putting a child in an isolation room makes about as much sense as putting a mentally ill adult into a prison's solitary confinement. But I was deferring to professionals the whole time while I was also trying to give myself a crash course in mental illness.

Staff told me most kids are in the isolation room for just a few hours. I never saw the room, but I imagined it was like a reception room, with a couch or some chairs. Like a "time out," or "detention," they are given something reflective to write, and usually the kids comply because they want to go back to being with their friends and routine. Not Noah. The staff was soon baffled to see that Noah preferred the isolation room, or at least he had no incentive to do what it takes to get out of there. He spent consecutive *weeks* in isolation and even the staff admitted they didn't know what to do with him. I also found out after the fact, there was even a period when he would only consume milk and he refused solid foods.

Noah also began to urinate on himself in the isolation room. He was obviously mentally deteriorating and it got to the point where they had to bribe him to leave. They began new protocols with Noah because he was not responding the way other kids would. Instead of granting rewards for good behavior, they started to offer rewards to Noah in *advance* of good behavior. They told him he could play the school piano as long as he followed the rules and other bargaining chips.

His dad and I would visit, schedules permitting; his dad was able to travel more easily than I could. The school property had a pleasant layout. It almost felt like a small college campus with newer looking buildings against the backdrop of majestic mountains. They had cottages where the students lived and an on-site church. I was also taken to see horses and stables, where some of the students learned to ride as part of their therapy.

Noah allowed for his hair to be cut shorter, but he now had some facial hair, scrappy, and not quite a full-grown beard. He had put on about ten pounds. When I visited, it felt repressive. Staff arranged for us to sit in one of the empty classrooms and I would bring him a meal from a local restaurant. Our conversations were superficial and Noah appeared cagey and guarded most of the time. He was clearly unhappy and justifiably resentful we had placed him there against his will. I tried to inspire him to plan for a brighter future and keep attending his classes, many of which he refused to go to. I brought a laptop and showed him a website for the Musician's Institute in Hollywood, where he could major in music and even learn how to make a guitar from scratch. The only pre-requisite for Musician's Institute was a high school diploma. We had already lowered our expectations a little in regards to his academic future. I still thought that was reachable, considering how Noah was identified as gifted from an early age.

Just a couple years prior, Noah had said he wanted to study sociology in college; not knowing his aunt had a Ph.D. in Sociology. Now I was just hoping he could graduate from high school. When Noah saw the website for the Musician's Institute, he just looked at me and said, "It feels like the world is an orange that you are smashing in my face."

The school was really at a loss as to how to help Noah and even looked into sending him to another program, in another state. No other residential schools wanted to accept a student who caused problems. He was stuck there and staff even suggested we hire an additional personal support aide to be by his side each day. Noah was practically catatonic and almost needed help putting one foot in front of the other. We hired an aid to be by his side, but it didn't help Noah become more functional or cooperative.

One time I left the school after a short visit with Noah, so frazzled and out of my own body that I sped through a red light while driving back to the airport. I didn't realize what I had done, until I saw from my peripheral view, trucks from both sides slamming on their brakes and missing my car by just a few feet. It could have been a spectacular multi-car crash. I saw my body ejected from the car, flying in the air, even though it didn't really happen. I kept going without braking, straight onto the freeway ramp, sweating and hoping no one would call the police and chase me down for running the red light.

In another memorable family visit, we met with the school principal, who was also acting as the prescribing doctor for all the students. I will refer to him as Dr. Fake. He sat in his chair with an aura of confidence and disdain. We questioned whether or not Noah was under-medicated and he assured us that he could make Noah as "docile as a doorknob" if he were to increase his medication, but that he didn't want to do that. He launched into a speech about how Noah was a dangerous combination of being both highly intelligent and highly manipulative. He claimed Noah was not mentally ill, but just pretending! Does a child stay in an isolation room, repeatedly for weeks at a time, only drinking milk and urinating on himself just to be manipulative?

I responded to Dr. Fake by saying Noah should win an Academy Award for his performance as a mentally ill person if that were the case. Dr. Fake slammed his fist on his desk and said, "Yes, he deserves an Academy Award." Much later, after Noah had left that horribly inappropriate school, I found out Dr. Fake was not a licensed psychiatrist. He had his medical degree in orthopedic surgery! That a school with hundreds of psychologically troubled teens did not have one competent psychiatrist is beyond belief. It is only now when I reflect on this do I believe this Mormon-run school was anti-psychiatry, in spite of how they marketed their program to the Department of Mental Health in Los Angeles.

As time goes by, many parents and caretakers become outraged by the endless incompetency. We begin to advocate more for our defenseless loved ones so we can prevent making the same mistakes or letting mental health providers get away with negligence. I can't go back in time, but I should have written a complaint to the Department of Mental Health, at the very least, to alert them as to the fraudulent behavior of the school they contracted. Years later I would go on-line and read some very critical Yelp reviews about the school, by former students as well as by their parents. (Social media can be a good tool for reality checks. You see past the marketing and get a range of experiences.)

About eight months into Noah being at that residential school, we had him escorted back to L.A. again for a couple of days, where he was formally tested so that he could be granted "IEP" status. This stands for Individualized Education Program and is afforded to any citizen of our United States, as they are legally entitled to an education. When it is determined that a child cannot function at home, they have to receive their education elsewhere. Up until the IEP was approved, Noah's father and I were splitting the costs of a $9,000 per month tuition (in 2007 dollars). We were convinced by the social workers who arranged for Noah's placement at the School, that we had to dig into (a non-existent) college fund to pay for it. Their mantra was that if we didn't invest the money in our son now, "there would be no college years later." I ended up getting an Equity Line of Credit against my house in order to pay my share. This is typical for families trying to find ways to pay for the treatment or care of their ill loved ones. We share in this financial stress with cancer patients and others who have mounting medical bills that can eventually bankrupt them.

Once the IEP was approved, the Department of Mental Health would pay for accommodations, and the Los Angeles Unified School District would pay the education part. They pick up the tab, but there would be no retroactive reimbursement. Through this process, Noah was officially identified as having a serious mental illness commencing as a minor, and that would become relevant years later, so at least it was well documented.

When Noah turned 17 ½, the school legally could not move him without his permission, so we rode it out until his 18th birthday before bringing him home, worse off than when he arrived there. The school had failed him, we had failed him, and I later learned that even the kids who got better while at the School had a very high relapse rate once they left. This was only the beginning of our mental illness journey, but I was already feeling tremendous stress and told myself I didn't care what happened to my business, the entire year would be focused on trying to help Noah get better. How do you help someone who doesn't recognize they have a brain illness? It's not their fault the brain can't inform itself that something's gone haywire.

FOUR:

5150

What is a (Fifty-One-Fifty) 5150? Well, in my youth, 5150 was simply the title of a Van Halen album; I never questioned it further. I assumed maybe it was the birth date of one of the band members, like David Lee Roth or Eddie Van Halen. In actuality, 5150 is the California law code for an involuntary 72-hour psychiatric hold, which can be levied by either law enforcement or credentialed mental health professionals. This keeps a person in the hospital at least three days and sometimes longer; the hold can be legally extended. To date, my son has been hospitalized nine times. He's been held for a few days, one to two weeks, two months, and the longest stint was for five months. The time he was in the hospital for five months was because he was waiting for a bed at a longer-term facility, called an IMD (Institute of Mental Disease). That's what they call a vacancy, "a bed." We'll get to that chapter in his life later.

Psychiatric hospitalizations can be very dramatic and depressing, for all involved. Almost no one visits my only son when he's hospitalized, except me and occasionally, his father. This is typical. Whenever I have put my name on a hospital sign-in sheet, there are very few names, relative to the number of patients there. I would go regularly and it brought up so many emotions each time. Of course, it goes without saying everything is worse for my son, as he is the one directly experiencing the torment of his mental illness. But parents and other family members go through their own special Hell also. We sheepishly enter these facilities, knowing some of the staff are sizing us up unfairly, speculating: What kind of parent raised this monster?

With the first hospitalization, we parents are often in shock and even question if it was necessary, even in the face of it being *so obviously* necessary. There is just so much stigma attached to it. No one sends flower arrangements or "Get Well" cards to people in psychiatric wards. They are lucky if family members care or dare to visit. By the time a loved one has been hospitalized numerous times, we are no longer in shock, but instead relieved, thinking "maybe this time something productive will happen!" I've met other parents whose son or daughter had been hospitalized many dozens of times. I once gave my son a Jimi Hendrix T-shirt while he was in the hospital and the next week when I visited, another patient was wearing it. It's like that with everything. We bring gifts that get stolen, thrown away, given away, sold or traded. We see our loved ones, who are otherwise physically healthy, wearing gowns, slippers, or the same dirty clothes because no one is really enforcing personal hygiene on them or insisting they change their clothes. There have been times when my son would rather throw away clothes than wash them, or even allow someone else to wash them.

We see displays of obsessive-compulsive disorder, often exacerbated in a hospital setting. Our loved one might not know what day it is, but they know if we are five minutes late to visit them! As we watch our loved one turn into another person, sometimes a person we hardly recognize, we realize we are the only ones who knew them before they became ill. For each parent, watching their son or daughter deteriorate, we can remember distinct "before" and "after" parts of their life.

Except for his father, and some aunts and uncles who haven't seen Noah in years, I am the only one who knows the "old Noah" before his illness emerged. I share these memories and thoughts as a parent, but siblings and other relatives go through similar pain when they witness their family member deteriorating, and with little or no resources to stop it. Medications aside, the illness itself has its own course and there is a period of years when the inflammation of the brain can undermine even a consistent treatment program.

The "before" Noah was such a joy to raise, every step of the way. I used to tell people I wanted another child just like him. But in truth, he was enough. He was such a funny kid, doing spot-on impressions. I used to tell people I was raising the next Robin Williams! After Robin Williams' suicide, the comparison became almost haunting. The "before" Noah fulfilled my dream of being a mother and I genuinely felt lucky to have him, until things started to unravel for him at age fifteen. Prior to that, Noah was a very popular, mellow, creative kid. He was also kind, never made fun of other kids, or had any enemies. Parents liked him and said he was always welcome in their home.

Teachers told me he was class clown, exceptionally bright and he always brought up interesting discussion points in class. Strangers would often stop and ask if Noah was an actor! People seemed to think they recognized him. He had a special glow or aura and he was very cute. With wire-rimmed glasses, he looked like a cross between the little boy from the *Jerry Maguire* movie to a light-haired Harry Potter.

I remember one time Noah had a slumber party with a half dozen friends. He was about ten years old. His friend Mike showed up with his medication for Tourette syndrome. Andrew brought his ADD medication and Jesse came with his anti-anxiety meds in tow. Each mother explained to me when her kid should take their meds and I had private thoughts about how lucky I was that my kid was normal! I dodged a bullet! Or so I thought. I had no real understanding of mental illness and most people don't until they are forced to deal with it.

I can look back with bittersweet irony, a couple of times when Noah and I encountered people with mental illness and how we reacted to it. One time, Noah was only about five or six years old and we were walking along an outdoor promenade in Santa Monica. There were various street performers, and many of them were creative types who probably held several jobs, including their gig on the promenade as a pantomime or a juggler.

We walked past one downtrodden fellow, sitting on the ground with a guitar. He wasn't one of the regular street musicians, engaging with the public, and taking requests for songs. No, this guy was clearly homeless, but he had his guitar case open for donations and he played his guitar, mostly for his own amusement. Noah got a very scared look on his face as we walked past this man and I asked Noah what was wrong. He said to me, "I hope I don't grow up to be a Ho-Bo." I was aghast. I couldn't even believe he would think like that and I didn't realize he even knew what a "Ho-Bo" was! I immediately told him that he was going to have a great life and not to have those worries.

About five years later, Noah and I were having lunch in a restaurant. A woman sat in a booth not too far away and she was making a ruckus, talking loudly to herself. Someone must have complained and in no time, a couple of waiters came to her booth and told her she had to leave. Somewhat against her will, they escorted her out and as she passed by our table, she said to no one in particular, "I'm starring in a movie that I don't even want to be in." I asked Noah if he understood what she meant, but he was speechless. I wanted him to have some compassion for the woman and not just think she was a weirdo.

I told Noah that what she said made perfect sense. I explained that she was feeling out of control, didn't like her life, and what was happening to her. Just before she got outside, I heard her say, "I feel like I'm in a barrel rolling down a hill." I could understand why she said that too. What they were doing with her, with each man holding one of her arms, probably felt something like being barreled out of there.

Little did I know that in a few years, I would also feel like I was starring in a movie I didn't want to be in and my son would feel the same. As we go through this process, where we compare the former child we knew and loved, with the shadow of who he became, it can test every fiber of our being to not succumb to our own depression and despair. At the very least, most parents hope their child will grow up to be a better version of themselves or a completely different person who will thrive from encouragement and opportunities the parent never had.

One time, the "after Noah" just looked at me with a stone-cold stare and said, "I just don't like being on this planet." As parents, we walk around with the grief and guilt that we brought someone into this world, a person who feels alienated by those around him, real or imagined. While we may not always "recognize" the person our ill loved one turns into, some people with schizophrenia experience something similar, but worse. Called Capgras Syndrome, the mentally ill person looks at people they know but believes they have been replaced by an imposter or a robot. I know a couple of mothers whose sons have Capgras Syndrome. When these men see their mothers, they inspect for every mole and freckle or distinguishing physical feature to make sure their mom is not an imposter. What a nightmare to imagine your closest relatives or friends are deceiving you. The loneliness must be crushing. One time, the "after Noah" admitted to me that when a person leaves the room and is not in his presence, he has a hard time believing they are real and have their own life to live.

Over the years, I have asked my son if he could tell me about what some of his perceptions and hallucinations have been like. I want to understand what he's going through, and I want him to know that he can confide in me. I also didn't want to rub it in his nose that he's experiencing a very different reality than most people. I don't want him to think that I am psychoanalyzing him or worse, making him re-live some very unpleasant experiences. But I do ask occasionally, as I am always interested in knowing if his medications are working or not. I don't want him to think I don't care or that I am oblivious to how hard it may be for him to even concentrate on our conversation. Is he, as the doctors would say, "responding to internal stimuli?" In one conversation where I asked Noah how come he doesn't like to take a shower, he told me that it makes his skin feel "soggy."

My son doesn't just have auditory hallucinations; he has them for every type of sensory input. He smells things that aren't there, like a room full of oranges or rancid meat. He might wear a jacket when it's hot outside, or no jacket when it is cold weather. He sees things that are not there, and one of the saddest hallucinations he had was seeing his musical idol Kurt Cobain appear in front of him and berate him. I've asked him if the voices he hears are familiar voices or strangers and he has said "both."

I asked him if he ever hears my voice when I'm not there and at first he said no, and then he said "sometimes." I hate knowing he has delusions about me; he once told a therapist I'd been brain-washed by the doctors. I hate knowing his own mind has conjured up my voice to say anything mean or derogatory to him; it's not the relationship we had. Unfortunately, many of the voices heard by people with schizophrenia are negative, demeaning, and destructive mandates. I don't know why the voices can't be nice, flattering, and encouraging. What deep, dark well of the subconscious do these voices come from? Sometimes the voices can be nice and even humorous. Researchers discovered that outside of American culture, auditory hallucinations are not as abusive or violent. I wonder why that is?

If Dr. Stephen Hawking believed there might be at least eleven dimensions, could a person with schizophrenia be tuned into some other dimensional frequency? In some cultures, the person with schizophrenia may have been held in higher regard, as if they were a high priest or shaman, in touch with other realms and spiritual insight. Could the voices be coming from something more mundane, like a brain that picks up on multiple radio transmissions? I'm sharing with you now the questions that come forth in my own mind, as a parent who struggles to accept and understand what is happening to my son.

I've read books on near-death experiences, where people who are pronounced dead can still hear and see things outside their body, which they could not have had any knowledge of. Could the schizophrenic brain be a receiver for other people's thoughts as well? More often, I think of the brain like a computer, where the schizophrenic mind has a computer-like virus with corrupted, inaccessible files, making memory and sequencing much more difficult, among many other problems with brain functioning.

Yet, as deluded as Noah has been about so many things, there have been times when he would assess a situation, or another person, exactly the same as I would, very perceptive and even with the eyes of a comedian. In Clifford Pickover's book, *Strange Brains and Genius: The Secret Lives of Eccentric Scientists and Madmen*, I found comfort reading about famous inventors and scientists from the 1800s who were mentally ill and still brilliant in their discoveries.

Often, Noah laughs to himself, and he tells me he was just thinking of something funny. I never know if he is actually listening to a voice outside of himself whispering something amusing. I talk to myself all the time, continuously, all day long, as many people do. But it's my own ego, my own personality. I've never heard someone else's voice that sounds like it is inside or just outside my own head. That must truly be a frightening experience and I don't know how anyone could ever get used to it.

FIVE:

Not So Sober Living

In May of 2009, Noah had just turned eighteen and was about to be discharged from the out-of-state school. I happened to hear from another parent about an outpatient therapy program not far from my home, which specialized in young adults from age eighteen to twenty-four years old. We really had no understanding of what we could do for our son upon his return and his father even offered to see if he could live at home while receiving outpatient treatment. We immediately got Noah signed up for this special outpatient program run by a delightful and inspiring psychotherapist named Dr. Coren.

Even before Noah got back into town, I started to attend Dr. Coren's free lectures about how to set boundaries with troubled teens and young adults. He gave me hope. Noah began to attend both private and group therapy four afternoons per week, and our private insurance began to foot the bill to the tune of $10,000 per month. Dr. Coren's staff suggested that Noah live in a Sober Living Home since it became evident immediately that he could not live with his dad without problems. The staff wanted to see Noah live with higher functioning people, as opposed to a Board and Care for adults with mental illness. Even though Noah did not have an illicit drug problem per se, he had been dabbling in drugs before we sent him out of state and he had no insight into how harmful they were for him. It goes without saying that substance abuse along with mental illness will always exacerbate the situation and many of the mentally ill seek relief in drugs. Noah did fit the profile of someone with addictions, now referred to as "Dual Diagnosis."

Noah was asked to leave several Sober Living Houses within a two-year period. He was stealing food and other items from housemates. He was breaking doorknobs and causing property damage. He didn't take the Alcoholics Anonymous 12-Step meetings seriously. He really was not in an appropriate environment for his needs. Sober Living homes have every type of people living under one roof. Some people voluntarily move into a Sober Living home, separating from family and friends in order to do the hard work of achieving sobriety. Some people are court-ordered into Sober Living and that presents a challenging dynamic for those who are more willing to address their addiction. Is this an appropriate place for an 18-year-old with schizophrenia? Once again I followed the advice of the experts though my gut told me otherwise.

Anyone considering having their mentally ill family member reside in a Sober Living House needs to make that decision very carefully. I later learned that some Sober Living directors are so strict about sobriety they even look down upon a person who uses prescription medication. There are even some Sober Living Houses that forbid their residents from using mouthwash unless it is totally alcohol-free. Certainly, it is not a long-term solution for a person with a long term illness.

I was new to the 12-Step philosophy and their recovery model when Noah began living in Sober Living houses. My boyfriend Ron, who I met shortly after Noah came back from the school in Utah, had been sober for over a decade and he spoke highly about the 12-step principles. I had reason to believe that keeping Noah away from street drugs would make addressing his mental illness easier. I was also hoping the 12-step approach might inspire Noah to quit smoking, but I came to realize that when people are battling drugs and alcohol, tobacco is considered a minor vice in comparison. It's quite common for 12-Steppers to socialize before and after their meetings with smoke breaks.

Ron had worked in the mental health care field as a case manager for twenty-four years. A week into dating him, he lost his job at a private agency where his caseload included a half dozen men and women with schizophrenia. Supposedly, Ron was a valued employee, but his boss was downsizing and they let Ron go because he was the only one in the office without a master's degree in social work. Ron began working in mental health while getting his BA in Psychology. He worked to pay his tuition. He certainly had the professional experience to qualify for continued employment in case management, but he soon found out that the whole field was requiring master's degrees. I felt I had been truly blessed to meet a man who knew so much about my son's illness and who didn't let it prevent him from wanting to be in a relationship with me. I was very attracted to Ron; he was 6' 2", had big blue eyes with grayish-brown hair and a goatee. From a certain angle, he looked like a young version of the country singer Kenny Rodgers.

Ron went on unemployment benefits and began searching for another job. With time on his hands, he did begin to help me with Noah. Ron was also a much-needed support system for me because it was around this same time that my ex-husband began to distance himself from Noah. It soon became obvious that I would be making all the important decisions regarding our son. I can't speak on his behalf or make projections about what my ex-husband's own perspective or turmoil caused him to do or not do. That would be his story to tell and I'll leave it at that.

One night we got a call from the Program Director at the third Sober Living House. No one had seen Noah since the afternoon and it was close to midnight. It was the first time Ron and I had planned a weekend mini-vacation, in San Diego. We had gotten there on a Friday afternoon and this call came later in the evening as we were about to go to sleep. The program director, Stuart, asked me if I had any idea where Noah might have gone. I could only suggest that maybe he had taken a bus somewhere, perhaps Venice Beach. Noah rarely had money with him, but I learned years later that many bus drivers took pity on him and let him ride the buses for free. Stuart called the local police and asked if they would do a courtesy search for him, even though Noah had not been missing for more than twenty-four hours.

I couldn't sleep that night, but I also knew that if we drove back to Los Angeles, trying to drive around at night and find him in a city with more than three million people would be a recipe for hysteria. We sat tight in the hotel room, waiting for more calls. Noah's dad was out of state and equally incapable of doing anything to help find Noah. The police called us next and asked a few questions about his physical appearance and where we thought he might be. About thirty minutes later, we got the call that no parent wants to get. It was now past midnight and the officer asked me for the contact number for Noah's dentist. I've watched enough Dateline episodes to know why they want access to dental records; they need to identify a body that way! I tried to stay calm, but it was one surreal conversation.

Around four in the morning, I got a call directly from Noah. He told me that he had taken a bus to the beach and didn't realize they stopped working at midnight. At some point in his journey back to the Sober Living house, the bus driver had to let him out and there were no connecting bus routes. Noah did recognize where he was and knew how to get to his dad's house. He walked several miles alone in the dark. With his father not being home, Noah told me that he sat on the driveway for a while and then the backyard. He did figure he needed to call and let someone know what happened.

Noah then walked another ¼ mile over to his father's place
of worship, where an all-night security guard let Noah use the
phone. They let him use the bathroom and spend the night inside,
but there was no one who could return him to his Sober Living
House, which was about five miles away. His father and I made
some calls and arranged for someone to pick up Noah by six in
the morning and take him back to where he lived. I didn't know
what the full consequences would be for this escapade, so Ron
and I canceled our weekend plans and returned in the morning as
well. I later learned the police officers who did a courtesy search
for him the night before showed up at the Sober Living House
the following morning. They were not pleased that resources were
spent looking for someone who was just out having a good time
at everyone else's expense. I don't recall if they had been informed
about my son's mental illness or not. They sternly warned him not
to do such a thing again.

Noah was wearing out his welcome at this third Sober Living
House. He was now making a nuisance of himself in the neighborhood by panhandling. Sober Living Houses always want to make a
good impression, or at least go unnoticed in residential areas. Noah
wanted more and more cigarettes; begging for money was how he
achieved his goal. For years, the smoking issue only made everything
about Noah's illness worse. Practically a chain-smoker, he made
it nearly impossible to participate in mandatory programs, indoor
activities, group sessions, and therapies. His body would wake him
up in the middle of the night from withdrawal symptoms, so his
addiction wouldn't even allow him a full night's sleep anymore.

The stench of cigarettes on his clothes, his hair, and coming
out of his pores made it hard to have Noah in my car or in my
home. In between every errand with him, I had to stand back
ten feet or stay in my car, while he sat on the ground, smoking
sometimes two cigarettes one after the other before he achieved

his nicotine levels. According to studies, 92% of all men with schizophrenia smoke. Reward centers in the brain light up twice as much in the brains of males with schizophrenia than those who don't have it. More bang for the buck. It gives them fleeting moments of mental clarity (sensory gating) and calm. My son's own nicotine addiction has made him do outrageous things, but I try to understand and be patient because smoking is one of the few things in life he has enjoyed doing since he became ill. How can I take that away from him or bother him to quit when it gives him so much relief?

While Noah lived at all of those Sober Living Houses, he was really failing to take care of his most basic needs, including making meals for himself. His counselor Jeff would take Noah shopping twice a week at a market for prepared foods. Often, Noah would eat all his food too quickly, days before the next scheduled shopping trip. His appetite was now insatiable due to antipsychotic medications. One weekend, Noah needed to stay with me, as he was in between Sober Living Houses. I was aghast when I saw what kind of food he was allowed to purchase with Jeff's approval for the three days he would stay with me. The therapy team wanted him to fend for himself, instead of having mom make his meals. This was part of their philosophy, to support more independence. He brought home a loaf of white bread, a couple of pounds of baloney, and a jar of mayonnaise. Noah's plan was to just eat three baloney sandwiches per day. I tabulated in my head the outrageous amount of fat and cholesterol this young man would be consuming. It was particularly heartbreaking to see how malnourished he was becoming, especially for a person who had been raised by "health nuts."

As soon as Noah got situated in his fourth and last Sober Living House, I agreed to prepare all his meals and deliver them each morning. I thought it was do-able because this new Sober

Living House was only eight minutes from my home. I made a month-long menu so that he would not get bored with the meals. I got up an hour earlier each morning to prepare these meals and also made extra for my boyfriend Ron and myself. I thought at the time I was just being organized and helping Noah get back some of his health through proper nutrition. Taking on the role of his personal chef could have been seen as "co-dependent" behavior according to some observers, but I felt an urgency to step in and take control where I could. Aside from Noah gaining a lot of weight in just a couple of years, he had very low energy and dark circles under his eyes.

I had a right to be concerned and those concerns turned into fears, which even the professionals eventually could not ignore. Just as one example, Noah had blood work done on a more regular basis than most young men in their twenties. At various times his lab work showed a vitamin D deficiency, which can exacerbate a lot of health problems, and increase depression. A few years later, he would have hypertension, high triglycerides, and high cholesterol. Noah's biological age would soon surpass his chronological age.

Noah never complained about the meals I made for him, delivered in to-go boxes like a restaurant delivery service. I learned later he sometimes traded his meals with other residents. I resigned myself to the fact that he would frequently trade, sell, and throw away things I worked hard to provide. Much of his social skills and his experience, or lack of experience, in garnering friends, would be established through trading items or giving things to people. Often, he would be tricked or bullied into giving away things like watches, shoes, and other clothing and personal belongings. To shove my sadness under the rug, I began to joke about how easy it was to shop for my son because he always needed "everything."

The accommodations were pretty nice at the last Sober Living House and Noah had his own bedroom. Noah was still not, however, even remotely stable. In fact, it would take years to realize he was not responding well to a dozen different antipsychotics, mood stabilizers, and combinations of medications. By now he had also tried Zyprexa and Risperidone. He even had one psychiatrist who was willing to take Noah off his meds since Noah expressed a desire to stop taking them without explaining why. For people with no insight into their illness, you can understand why they would not see the value in taking medication. Others, who are medication compliant for a while, often assume they can stop taking their meds once they feel better, as if anti-psychotics were antibiotics.

I brought Noah in to see his psychiatrist at the time, Dr. Twain, and basically told the both of them that if Noah went off his medication I would not pay for his rent and he would end up homeless. I don't know if I would have made good on that ultimatum, but Noah spent a half-day outside and then returned to the Sober Living House. He decided he did not want to be homeless and resumed taking his meds. I was pretty disturbed by Dr. Twain's nonchalance on the matter. He didn't say much to dissuade Noah from stopping his medication, nor did he recommend tapering off slowly. Over the years, more psychiatrists would make bad decisions in regards to my son. I am sorry to report that I have learned these lapses in professional judgment are common. I'm not anti-psychiatry and there are certainly good psychiatrists, but we had not found a good one yet.

Noah later punched a hole in the wall at the last Sober Living House and they asked him to leave. This would become his M.O. for getting evicted from residences to come. At this point, I felt he needed a higher level of care than Sober Living Houses. I naively felt he really should be in a licensed Board and Care for adults with mental illness.

SIX:

Boundaries
and Consequences

I found a list on-line of Board and Cares and chose the one that was closest to Noah's therapist. It was a crowded apartment building conversion with over a hundred residents and I quickly learned what depressing places these Board and Cares can be. I also learned years later, that because Noah was receiving SSI benefits (provided by the Federal government), he should have had a case manager working with us to find appropriate housing. That information didn't come to me until I got more involved with my local chapter of NAMI (National Alliance on Mental Illness.)

The only immediate benefit with these Board and Cares is they provided meals he agreed to eat and they administered medications. I asked the staff to dole out his cigarettes and he became a real pest, always asking them for a cigarette ahead of schedule. He would camp out in front of the staff office in the early hours of the morning before the staff arrived; he was just living to smoke. In the back of my mind, I often thought about his father's mother, who was a smoker in her youth. She quit for the sake of her kids, but ended up battling breast cancer and then lung cancer twice before she died, when Noah was seventeen. He lost his other grandmother, my mom, when he was only ten.

One of the last things my mother said, after her brain cancer diagnosis, was directly to Noah at her bedside in the hospital. She said, "I want to see you graduate from college." She was only 72 years old, but hoping to live to at least 84, like her own mother. Instead, she passed away three weeks later and Noah never would see college.

Noah had his own room at this first state licensed Board and Care, but it was the size of a large walk-in closet and he continued to be cagey and volatile. Ron was helping out by driving Noah from the Board and Care to his therapy sessions four days per week. At Dr. Coren's office they were getting annoyed with Noah because he was becoming a nuisance to the whole building. At each break in between therapy sessions, he was panhandling to people coming and going from this professional building. They were going to discharge him as a client if he didn't stop. Noah's father and I are middle-class professionals; he wasn't raised this way and was never around this kind of influence. His grandpa, Dr. Jack would be rolling in his grave if he saw what his grandson was turning into and how helpless we were to stop it. Between Noah's father and I, our combined families included doctors, lawyers, architects, consultants, authors, and University professors. If my son was destined to be a starving musician, I could have easily supported that as long as he was happy, feeling creative and with a sense of purpose and friends. Instead, each day he seemed to get closer and closer to the "Ho-Bo" he once feared he would become, as if it were a premonition.

Within the mental health community, there is a lot of discussion about stigma for the mentally ill person, but not as much about the stigma felt by and against parents. There are also notions about how people from various cultures, races and religions handle this tragedy differently. At the end of the day, we all grieve in similar fashion. An untimely death for an ill loved one is horrible to bear, but at least there is some finality. With a chronically, seriously mentally ill family member, the sense of loss can go on for decades.

Before the decision could be made by Dr. Coren and his team to release Noah as a client, his insurance stopped paying for the hefty therapy bills. The support system we had painstakingly created ended abruptly and in one day. At the Board and Care, Noah started picking at the drywall in his room. As opposed to punching a hole in the wall, he was just picking away at it. It wasn't until the hole was the size of a stop sign that the staff brought it to my attention. He was definitely angry, but it was also the result of some obsessive-compulsive tendencies emerging as well.

When Noah was confronted about the damage, he blamed the wall. According to Noah, it was the wall's fault because it was so easy for him to pick away at the thin drywall in this old dilapidated building. Years later I would find out that this particular Board and Care had a chronic bed bug infestation. The owners had no capacity to safely transfer 130 residents out of the facility, treat the whole building, and also insure that the residents would have all their belongings effectively fumigated or replaced. I have a friend whose son lived at that same Board and Care a few years after Noah lived there. When she found out about the bed bugs, she would make her son change all his clothes in the garage, with clean ones she provided him with, before he could enter her house for any visit. He didn't come to visit often, but her house still got infested. These are just some of the disgusting aspects we parents take in stride when our children become part of this vulnerable population; it becomes our new normal.

When we visit our loved one in a typical Board and Care, sometimes they are living just a notch or two above abject squalor. Housekeepers do perfunctory cleaning of the resident bedrooms, emptying trash and sweeping floors, but it must be depressing for staff. With Noah's inability to take care of his own laundry, I'd see piles of dirty clothes on the floor or shoved in the closet, mixed up with the clean clothes. Food and food wrappers strewn about and the Board and Care bedrooms can look as if they've been hit by a tornado. During times when Noah violated the No Smoking Indoors rule, his bedroom looked like a giant ashtray. Not every resident maintains a pig sty, but those who are unstable and miserable have no energy to maintain basic cleanliness. Their small personal space becomes a reflection of their own state of mind.

I also developed my own solution for transporting my son, with his atrocious lack of personal hygiene. For a long time, the passenger seat in my car was covered with a heavy-duty plastic lawn leaf bag, with a towel on top and then covered over with a washable sheep-skin seat cover. I washed the towel and seat cover frequently. I also put a box in the trunk of my car with an extra set of clothes and shoes for Noah, water, protein bars, packs of cigarettes, and some important papers and documentation regarding his mental illness. I was ready at a moment's notice to pick him up, take him to a hospital or give the Mobile Psych Evaluation Team important information they would need if we met up during an emergency.

Noah had two separate eight-day hospitalizations while being at this Board and Care in 2011. The second one was voluntary. It became clear to me then the short-term hospitalizations could hardly promise any return to stability. The duration of his hospital stays had everything to do with insurance coverage limitations and nothing to do with proper treatment. A psychiatrist will concur that it can take four or more weeks for someone to stabilize on a new medication; for insurance companies, "stabilization" is achieved when they determine they have paid their limit.

When Noah was asked to leave this Board and Care, I once again began to ponder what kind of facility would be more appropriate and more acceptable to him. My once popular son had now been four years without having a true friend. I found a Board and Care about thirty miles away which claimed to have a younger population of residents. In my visits to various Board and Cares, I began to see the average age of residents was in their forties. Some were much older and some in their thirties, but not so many in their twenties. Why not? I asked questions and came to my own conclusions. I reasoned that many unstable people in their twenties were still living at home with parents, who were grappling with a mental illness that recently emerged. Many parents were putting up with intolerable and dangerous circumstances but were also clueless as to what to do. Most lacked resources for these very expensive private treatment programs. Even I had scanned the internet for private facilities across the country. Some of these residential programs charge as much as $5,000.00 to $20,000 *per month!*

Some younger adults are hiding out in college or living on their own, but failing miserably and acting erratically. Family members can be unaware their loved one is seriously ill since they are not witnessing the deterioration daily. Plenty of men in their twenties operate with undiagnosed and untreated mental illness that propels them into the criminal justice system where they are housed in jails instead of mental health facilities. Mentally ill women, to a much lesser extent, also end up incarcerated. More often, they are in Board and Cares or their behaviors are less threatening and more bearable for family members who keep them at home.

Still, I heard countless stories about mentally ill women at my NAMI Family Support meetings, stories as equally exasperating and heart-breaking. One friend has a chronically depressed daughter at home. She greets her mother each morning with the first words that come out of her mouth every day, "I don't want to live anymore." Her mother feels like a hostage in her own home, afraid to leave her daughter alone too long and giving her daughter pep talks several times a day.

When our mentally ill son or daughter is stable, we still hold our breath because we know relapses are common and highly likely. When they are unstable, we don't know if they will harm themselves, animals, or other people. With no malice intent, we just don't know if they will do something forgetful like fall asleep smoking in bed. Will this person burn the house down? Will they accidentally start a brush fire that ends up causing millions of dollars in property damage? Will the stress of it all cut five or ten years off our lives? I worry more often about what will happen to my son, without any brother or sister, after I'm gone. If I'm lucky enough to leave him an inheritance, will people take advantage and steal from him? Will there be anyone in his life he can call a friend and who he can rely on for good advice and protection?

Another NAMI Mom told us in a family support meeting about her daughter living hundreds of miles away. She had once been a successful massage therapist but the mental illness took over and her daughter became obsessively compulsive about being clean. The daughter had a sustained delusion her body was covered in shit; she bathed around eight times a day and spent much of her waking hours in the shower! This NAMI Mom came to our meeting hoping members could tell her how to arrange for Wellness Checks on her daughter since she couldn't be there in person. How do we sleep at night? Sometimes we don't.

One of the mottos in the NAMI meetings is to "not judge anyone's pain as less than our own." This was sometimes a challenge for me. A few times, mothers came to our meetings to vent about their college-aged children who experienced bouts of depression and needed to take a break from college or reduce their classes. College! What a dream that was! I wished I could trade their problems for ours.

Even a diagnosis like Obsessive Compulsive Disorder can be as severe and debilitating as schizophrenia. One lady came to a meeting to discuss her daughter with severe OCD and she certainly had everyone's sympathy. In the case of her daughter, if she walked down the street and passed a person who she thought looked at her strange, her daughter would have to go home immediately. Not only did she have to change the clothes that the stranger "ruined," she would never wear the clothes again! Washing the stranger's energy off the clothes wasn't good enough. The mother sighed and said she now shops at Target for her daughter's clothes, spending as little as possible since she knows the clothes won't last long. Additionally, if her daughter didn't like some meal made for her at home, the contents of the entire refrigerator had to be thrown out. I hope and pray that this young woman has since gotten the help she needed.

When I found a Board and Care that claimed to have younger people, I was naively hopeful Noah would find some semblance of friendship with other young people with similar interests. Not exactly "summer camp," but at least other people he could relate to. Of course, it has to be said that Noah was just a shadow of his former self. His passions and hobbies were greatly diminished and Noah was spending a lot of time sleeping, smoking, and staring at the walls. Even when he was aware that other residents were musical, he had no motivation to play music with anyone else.

The child who once bolted down the stairs to interrupt my phone conversation, shouting, "I need action!" when he wanted to play at the park, no longer existed.

Some of the most precocious things he said to me came at the ages of two and three. One day, I was "scolding" him in a playful, pretend way. He understood I was kidding and after I gave him a fake ultimatum, he shot back a direct quote from Jiminy Cricket in the Pinocchio movie and said, "Always let your conscience be your guide." This playfulness continued and he seemed to enjoy cracking me up regularly. On one rare occasion when he was acting naughty, I told Noah he needed to apologize and make it a really sincere apology, after one attempt where he sarcastically rolled his eyes. He was now eight years old and witty beyond his years. It took him more than fifteen minutes to come out of his bedroom, but he had a very self-satisfied look on his face. He cozied up to my arm, looked up with a sweet impish smile, and said, "I'm sorry.com."

As a young teen who could maintain focus and play his guitar or bass for hours a day, a decade later he could only focus on something for a few minutes at a time, if that. Back in middle school, almost everyone knew that Noah was a musical prodigy. There was a running joke between his guitar teacher, Ted, and I. Every other time he saw me, Ted would say as if for the first time, "You DO know your son is going to be a professional musician, right?"

One night, his eighth-grade class performed a musical and I attended not knowing in advance what part Noah would play. Some of the kids in his class were exceptional singers, but the school hired professional adult musicians to accompany them for the show. When the lights came on, Noah sat at the side of the stage among the professional adult musicians, not playing guitar or bass, but the drums! Noah never had a drum lesson; this was the surprise of the evening for me! He was jamming with the adults like an impromptu studio musician.

As a younger child, his drawings of Bart Simpson and the Teenage Mutant Ninja Turtles impressed his art teachers so much they displayed them on the classroom wall. The biggest hit was a portrait of his third-grade teacher, Mr. Short. Noah captured Mr. Short's expression and personality so well that it was taped up in the hallway for the whole school to see. When the illness set in, Noah lost his ability to draw. Now he just scribbles on page after page in journal notebooks from the Dollar Tree store. With 100% Jewish ancestry, he sometimes draws pages of swastikas. When I have questioned his "art," he reminds me that Hitler stole this once benign symbol from Hinduism.

The child who was always hungry for knowledge and conversation was gone. Schizophrenia causes the brain to malfunction in a multitude of ways; it's not even considered one disease, but a cluster or spectrum of brain dysfunctions. A person with schizophrenia, who also has paranoia, will present differently than one who does not have paranoia, or OCD or a mood disorder, or substance abuse.

Depending on which parts of the brain are affected, some people with schizophrenia can still function superbly in an intellectual capacity, even when not totally stable, or when falling apart in other areas of their life. Dr. Elyn Saks, Chair Professor of Law at USC's Gould School of Law, wrote her memoir in 2008, *The Center Cannot Hold: My Journey Through Madness.* She recounts being able to get high grades in her courses at Yale, even when she was actively psychotic, telling her psychiatrist she wanted to kill him, and attempting to jump off-campus buildings. For her, it's a good thing she didn't follow the advice of one of her therapists when young. That therapist wanted her to set her expectations lower and go for a less stressful job, like working as a cashier.

My son is not in the category where he can excel academically despite having delusions, paranoia, or hallucinations. Even though it has become almost politically incorrect to say someone is "schizophrenic," this disease often defines him from a functional standpoint. It brings me, as a mother, many regrets in knowing his intellectual and artistic potential will almost certainly never be realized. Noah's disease has ravaged parts of his brain and his ability to concentrate as well as his short-term memory is severely disabled.

Noah ended up not making friends at the second Board and Care, despite living there for two and a half years. During that time we sought out other sources of support for him since these

Board and Cares do not provide much more than food and shelter. I hired a GED coach to work with him, but it was fruitless because Noah couldn't concentrate. The GED instructor was young and could not be expected to understand the scope of Noah's illness. She suggested to him that he request ADD medication from his doctor. She didn't know that ADD medication can catapult a person with schizophrenia into a manic episode.

Noah agreed to go to eight months of neuro-feedback sessions, but we had to bargain with him and he was only willing to go if he could be taken out to lunch afterward. As far as we could tell, the neuro-feedback did not help with his cognitive function or improve his short-term memory at all. This is just one of the "wonder cures" marketed to parents, desperate to find treatment, therapies, supplements, and nutritional regimes that supposedly help schizophrenia. No doubt, some of these "off label" and unconventional practices do work, to some degree, for some people. But they don't help all of the people, all of the time, and end up being rather expensive and a waste of time for many. How many well-meaning but ignorant people did I listen to as they suggested that a gluten-free diet or art therapy would somehow make a significant difference?

Caring parents are searching for the Holy Grail of recovery from mental illness, only to find false hope much of the time. Whatever you decide to do or try, follow through with some due diligence and get second and third opinions. I didn't investigate the track record for neuro-feedback and schizophrenia when I should have, before committing to a long-term program. I've also seen that some therapies and supplements work better holistically, one complementing the other and not used in isolation. It should be noted there really is no cure for schizophrenia and no "recovery" in the traditional definition of the word. There is no "remission" from the illness like an absence of disease. By recovery, I am implying higher-functionality and the control or stable management of the most debilitating symptoms.

Around this time, in 2012 and 2013, I did hear about a Peer Coach with a good reputation for helping people with serious mental illness (SMI). He could gain their trust, have candid discussions with his clients, takes them on social outings, and help move the ill person in a positive direction. This Peer Coach had himself "recovered" in tangible and impressive ways. Also diagnosed with schizophrenia in his twenties, and having to drop out of college for a while, he eventually regained his footing and got a Master's degree in social work. I looked to this Peer Coach, then in his early forties, as a role model for Noah and hoped they would work together a long time. We did notice some improvement in my son's interest to do more than stare at the walls and break up his chronic isolation. Due to circumstances we could not control, those regular peer-coaching sessions came to a premature end. Having an ally or trusted companion can go a long way in helping the mentally ill person gain more motivation to try new things. At some point, family members often have to acknowledge that their ill loved one may respond more positively to suggestions made by a non-family member.

My boyfriend was also trying to make headway with Noah. As a former case manager, Ron had assisted many clients with schizophrenia and he wanted to help Noah as much as he could. For a time, he was traveling sixty miles round trip, twice a week, to play basketball with Noah and then take him out to lunch. For all practical purposes, Noah was becoming a stepson. Noah began to say that he didn't want to play basketball and just wanted to go out to eat. As I write this, I am surprised we didn't think of some alternative creative solution to break through my son's resistance. Perhaps he would have agreed to some other form of exercise or some other therapeutic activity. Instead, Ron drew a hard line in the sand: "No exercise, no lunch out. Period."

Their time together ended abruptly and their relationship suffered because of the lack of flexibility. Their relationship would suffer even more as time went on and my relationship with Ron would deteriorate because of the mounting tension in our different "parenting" styles. Discussions about *boundaries and consequences* took their toll over time, as I was also getting conflicting advice from my NAMI family support group. Ron argued that as a case manager he was often given clients who were so difficult, other case managers did not want to work with them. Ron told me his strong disciplinary consistency contributed directly to his clients getting better, where they showed more respect and consideration for others. It was hard for me to imagine Ron being so stern with his clients. Around me, he had a timid, soft-spoken disposition. He also had ingrained programming from his abusive childhood. He wanted to help any who were psychologically vulnerable; this was a man who would jump out of his car and stop traffic so that a dog could safely cross the street.

One of the common realities when dealing with mentally ill people is that even though they may have greatly diminished capacity to care for themselves and make good decisions, they may also be stubborn and reject unsolicited advice. If Ron was waiting for Noah to call him, apologize, and say that he would again agree to play basketball before going out to lunch, that call never came.

For most people with serious mental illness, it is hard for them to feel or show empathy toward others. They may appear self-absorbed and in some ways, they are, lost in their thoughts. I remember one day my son called me to apologize for losing a book I had loaned him. He explained that he was sitting outside the Board and Care when a fire truck screamed by and frightened him. He jumped up and ran into the Board and Care to get away from the sound and commotion unfolding right on the street. When he returned outside, the book was nowhere to be found.

He told me to buy myself another book with the money I would have given him as an allowance.

As he was saying these words and apologizing over and over for losing the book, I found myself amazed at how thoughtful, regretful, and concerned he was. He showed a level of empathy I had not seen since before his illness. In the back of my mind, I wondered what kind of drug he was on, perhaps Ecstasy, the "love drug." I said to myself, "whatever drug he's on, it's a good one for a change. He should stay on it!" This was in sharp contrast to crystal meth and other drugs he took which intensified his alienation and perpetuated his bad mood. While that display of effusive empathy was an isolated incident, my speculation was not so far-fetched. Years later I would attend a presentation by a psychiatrist from UCLA who said that research was being done with the "love drug" for people with schizophrenia, precisely to help them feel empathy and a connection to other people!

Ron seemed to be bothered by Noah's lack of empathy even more than me. He claimed his strict mandates with clients were eventually always honored. He had one client with schizophrenia whose personal hygiene was pretty bad when they first met. Before going on an outing, Ron insisted on numerous occasions that this man go back in his house, change his clothes, or even shower before Ron would let him in his car. Ron would even step into the man's bathroom to make sure he was taking a shower; this patient was a good example of a person who probably should not have been living on his own.

I believed Ron when he said he stood firmly on agreements he made with clients and got them to become more considerate and aware that the world didn't just revolve around them. I still found Ron's stance odd, however, given how cruel his parents were to him as a child. I couldn't integrate into my mind how he could assume the persona of such a strict authoritarian when he knew from personal experience how fragile a damaged psyche is. He knew all too well how a suffering person will shut down inside and retreat into their despair, not even aware of other people, let alone considerate of their wants and needs. Ron had told me about horrific abuses inflicted by his mother. The stories almost rivaled the incomprehensible news reports we hear about children locked in basements or chained to their beds by perverted parents who eventually get caught and shock the world. Back in the 1970s, Ron's mother got away with all her verbal and physical abuse against her children.

On Christmas Eve when Ron was nine years old, his mother Mabel was charged with attempted murder and felony child endangerment. A violent alcoholic, she threw Ron's older sister out a window, shattering the pane of glass. She also bit Ron's cheek that night. When the police arrived, Ron's mother and father were both drunk and no other relatives could be reached, so the police thought Ron would be safest in Juvenile Hall. Ron ended up staying at Juvenile Hall for over a month and was further traumatized by the older boys and bullies. He was finally released to his grandmother, who he stayed with for just a month while Mabel received counseling. She should have gone to jail for that as well as countless other daily acts of violence against her children. On the occasions when his parents had guests over at the house, Ron and his sisters would ask the guests to stay as long as possible as they knew their mother would go from Dr. Jekyll to Mr. Hyde as soon as the guests left.

Ron told me he ran away from home many times, to the police station or the fire department, begging for help. But each time he was returned to his mother, she acted innocently and put on a good performance to hide her sociopathic behavior. I asked Ron if his mother was attractive because I envisioned her being able to sweet-talk anyone considering pressing charges against her. Ron confirmed Mabel looked like a young Elizabeth Taylor and she acted like Mother of the Year when other people were around. This is the same woman who would beat Ron so badly she sent him off to grade school with make-up foundation on his arms and face to cover the bruises. This was the same woman who went on rages, busting into Ron's bedroom, turning over his 60-gallon aquarium and hitting him over the head with a frying pan. He had more than one concussion as well as long term neck and back problems.

Ron's "formative" years were spent in terror day in and day out, with his father as a co-conspirator, usually escaping the house to spend a night in a hotel when Mabel started throwing dishes. He left the children in harm's way regularly. After the third time his wife set the living room drapes on fire, Ron's father finally divorced Mabel. It's no wonder that Ron became an alcoholic, and plagued the rest of his life with Post Traumatic Stress Disorder, Anxiety, and Depression. Years later, Mabel would successfully commit suicide, leaving a note blaming her children. In 2004, Ron attempted suicide twice. His older sister brought him into her home for a while to sort it all out. Ron's past and his parallel universe was a graphic backdrop to what I was dealing with constantly with Noah.

Ron had the professional training and decades of experience to help people with schizophrenia, yet he never sought therapy for the abuse inflicted on him by Mabel because he said he could not financially afford it. Ron became a walking contradiction because he lived his whole adult life without the needed psychotherapy which he knew was so vital to the patients he interacted with. He maintained his sobriety, without continuing to go to meetings and without any friends besides me. At times he fit the profile of a "dry drunk."

NAMI stands for the National Alliance On Mental Illness and there are local chapters all over the country. One item gets discussed frequently in NAMI family support groups, as well as in 12-Step groups; make contracts and agreements with your mentally ill loved one, but only make a pact you can uphold or follow through on. Contracts and agreements must be realistic, however. The rigorous personal accounting an individual puts themselves through in Alcoholics Anonymous is not the same kind of contract a person with schizophrenia can be expected to honor. This is not to say that people with mental illness can't follow through on a promise. Many can and do. Many are so stubborn we can only pray they will use their strong convictions for something constructive one day. Noah always had a streak of stubbornness. Before his illness emerged, I jokingly gave him the Rap name, "Tenacious N."

But unlike alcoholism or drug addiction, mentally ill people often do *not* "hit rock bottom" and experience the humility and awareness needed to make drastic, sudden changes in their life and attitude. More often with mental illness, we see gradual changes that can be measured over months or even years. Since half the people with schizophrenia lack insight into their illness and believe their delusions, it is incredibly challenging and even unrealistic to set the same goals or at least the same timeline for change as people without serious mental illness.

In one memorable incident, Ron was very critical in terms of how I handled an agreement I made with my son. As a result, he thought I was weak and had undermined Noah's progress. More so, he thought I enabled Noah's anti-social behavior. The backdrop to this incident is that my son, like so many others on anti-psychotic medication, had gained a lot of weight in just a few years. He now looked like a chubby disheveled Seth Rogan. To inspire Noah to lose weight, I contracted to reward him with five dollars for every pound lost.

From the get-go, this was not the best plan to initiate with my son. He lived at a Board and Care where he had no control over the food he was served. Board and Care food is typically not healthy, not always fresh, and overloaded with sugary carbohydrates. Additionally, my son never even expressed a desire to lose weight. This was a goal I had for him; he probably thought I was being rude and judgmental. I can concur that if my mother had harped on me needing to lose weight when I was in my early twenties, I probably would have told her to mind her own business.

The plan, which my son agreed to passively, was that I would give him five dollars for every pound lost and he would get on the scale before going out for our weekly Saturday lunch. This verbal contract stated he would not get any money if he didn't lose weight, but the clincher was we wouldn't go out to eat if he *gained* weight. This was a setup for failure; I hadn't even thought through how my son would feel if we showed up to take him out to lunch, only to say, "sorry, see you next week" and leave if he had gained weight.

The first week Noah lost a pound and I thought he was motivated, not realizing the randomness of the weight loss. I had given him stevia packets to sweeten his tea and believed he might not be drinking so many sugary sodas, to account for the first pound. He even lost another pound the second week. I thought he was motivated to make the extra money, which he would, ironically, spend on more cigarettes. The following week he did not lose weight, so I didn't give him any money, and we proceeded to go out to eat. Then the inevitable happened; he gained weight one week. We had driven over thirty miles to see him and this was his only social outlet, seeing his mom and her boyfriend. I couldn't follow through with the contract to not take him out to lunch.

At that moment I realized what a naively planned, thoughtless contract I had created. I couldn't go through with it and just turn around and go home. Instead, I revised the agreement on the spot, said that if he were to gain weight, I would have a say in what he chose to eat for lunch and he could only drink green tea and no sugary sodas. That was okay with Noah. Taking Noah to lunch was closer to our stated goal to eat a healthy meal rather than the crap served at the Board and Care.

Ron was disgusted with me. He couldn't believe I didn't hold my ground and follow exactly the contract I had created. He believed the hard line approach is what worked with his schizophrenic clients in the past and would work with Noah.

As opposed to just being a weak enabler, I honestly didn't grasp how unfair and weird the contract was until I was faced with upholding it. This is just one example of how Ron and I didn't always share the same views on how to deal with my son.

These are the kinds of tensions that continued to mount until Ron and I had to come to terms with the fact I couldn't follow all of his recommendations.

Differences in opinion on how to handle a mentally ill child are also extremely common between spouses, still together or divorced. What was missing in Ron's resume of training and experience was a normal, loving parent-child relationship in his own family. Many other people tried to comfort me for the decisions I continued to make on my own, reminding me that Ron had no children of his own. He could not possibly understand the bond of unconditional love, and the torture a parent goes through with a mentally ill son or daughter. Ron had two of the worst parents I have ever heard of. He never received unconditional love from his mother or father, making it impossible for him to understand what would make me "cave" or how I wanted so much to preserve the relationship with Noah. Ron spent his whole life running away from his cruel parents, so he had no personal reference point as to why I was responding to my son with such leniency.

When Ron and I first met, he told me on our first date how fulfilling it was for him to work with a psychotic person, get them the services they needed and bring them to a place of stability. I might have fallen in love with him that night. I assumed he would be a great influence on Noah, but as time went by and I could not follow all of his advice, Ron participated less and less in the heavy decisions I had to make on Noah's behalf.

I also didn't want to burden Ron with helping me constantly with Noah, as Ron was struggling himself to stay afloat emotionally, physically, and psychologically. He started a woodworking business, which failed within the first year due to a lack of customers. But worse, he further injured his back and neck from working with heavy machinery. One day he came home from the woodshop, saying his whole right side was numb and later constant nerve pain would not let up. X-rays revealed serious degenerative disc disease. Ron also became a victim of the Medical Industrial Complex, with lousy doctors and pain management specialists, who consistently under-medicated him, presumably out of concern that he would abuse the highly addictive painkillers. He tried acupuncture, chiropractic adjustments, meditation, and epidurals, getting no relief from any of them. Lying down for hours a day, with an ice pack on his back, became the norm.

The only thing that cheered him up was our getting a golden retriever puppy; I named her Nutmeg. He spent almost every waking hour with her and she promptly became his emotional support dog.

SEVEN:

Crazy Is the New Normal

Still relatively new to the Board and Care experience, I thought there must be a better Board and Care where Noah could live, not just be "warehoused." He had lived at the "Manor" for more than two years and there was not much progress. He also continued to complain about being bullied by other young men living there. This was a Board and Care that housed over a hundred people and I got the feeling he might do better in an environment with fewer residents.

One of the worst aspects of Board and Care living is they are loud and have too many occupants. Here we have people suffering from hallucinations and paranoia, and yet they are placed in Board and Cares where the environment itself could easily aggravate all of their symptoms. People with schizophrenia should, ideally, be in low-stress environments if there is any hope of functional recovery. Many of these boards and Cares are in unsafe or poor neighborhoods because the more affluent areas are unaffordable to the Board and Care operators. Many communities protest at city councils and zoning boards against having housing in their neighborhoods as well.

The defined outside space for smoking was getting more restricted at the Manor and Noah started to resent the extra time it would take him to get over to the designated outside smoking area. This was a big deal for him because he was smoking two or more packs a day (40-plus cigarettes). His third-floor bedroom was a blessing in that it forced him to go up and down those flights of stairs many times per day. Privately, I thought it was fine because he was getting that much more exercise; he did end up losing twenty pounds over two years. But Noah started to challenge the rules and was caught more than once smoking on the third-floor balcony. The program director was simultaneously trying to find Noah a first-floor room he could move to, but also giving me signals that he may have to evict him.

I pre-empted the eviction and quickly found a one-story Board and Care a few miles away with only thirty-eight beds in a newly renovated building, including new furniture in each unit. With a menu that looked healthier than most Board and Cares, I started to believe maybe there really were better Board and Cares and we just hadn't experienced one yet. Those hopes were dashed when Noah got evicted from this smaller Board and Care just five months later. He had been caught on surveillance cameras smoking pot on the patio and inside his bathroom. After living thirty miles away in Pasadena for almost three years, I figured he might as well live closer to me in Los Angeles. I began to search for Board and Cares much closer to home, a stressful task on many fronts. Aside from the time it took from my job, it was difficult to find a new Board and Care quickly. New Program Directors wanted to know why Noah needed to move.

Firstly, there is a housing crisis for people with mental illness and it is one reason so many end up homeless. Next, it becomes a challenge to get a place for a mentally ill person if it becomes known they have cycled through many and have had evictions. I found myself in very awkward positions where I did not want to lie to the prospective Board and Care owners about Noah's history of property damage and non-compliance. Some of the worst places were willing to take a chance on him, just to fill a bed and receive more funding.

One day when I was frantically trying to coordinate an inter-view for Noah at a new Board and Care, he texted me. This was when he had a cell phone: before he had sold a half dozen phones and I had to let him get by without one, an example of how I was slow to execute boundaries and consequences. I never thought of a cell phone as a luxury item. I felt, and still do, that it's a lifeline for such a needy, disabled person. By this time, I had lost most of the leverage I used to have with Noah. I couldn't even withhold or reward him with money for things I wanted him to do. He got so good at panhandling he didn't need to accommodate my wishes for a financial reward. His text to me read, "Oh, by the way, I'm gay." I didn't respond to the text at all, but smiled inside, thinking, "That is the *least* of your problems." I also know my son likes to give new meaning to words and that "gay" to him might mean something else entirely than the current definition of the word.

Two weeks later he was in a fleeting relationship with a young woman at the new Board and Care. She ended up going AWOL. In two weeks, he thought he had a girlfriend, who he also thought became pregnant (she wasn't) and who he would have to marry if she were! An unwanted pregnancy can be a real nightmare for a seriously mentally ill person, incapable of handling such a responsibility. Additionally, there is a higher chance the child could end up with mental illness also. It is a hypothetical situation that I have thought about, like so many other worries. What would I do if my son became a father, without the ability to take on that role in any productive way? I've heard of people raising their grandchildren. Would I or could I ever do it? I felt bad for this young girl; she was nineteen years old and missing for a week. I heard she got hospitalized, but never returned to the Board and Care where she met Noah.

When it comes to wordplay, my son has created new definitions for many words and phrases. He once asked me if I knew the difference between an "artist" and a "musician." I was startled by the question but I proceeded to say an artist is someone who creates interesting things to look at with a variety of mediums like painting, drawing, and sculpting. I gave him my definition of a musician as someone who plays a musical instrument and/or composes music. Noah then told me that a musician is someone who just wants everyone to like them and think they are cool. He said an artist does what they want and they don't care what other people think. I asked him if he considered himself a musician or an artist, and he told me he was an artist. Even though he was an accomplished musician, I did understand his nuanced way of describing an artist and musician the way he did. These are the kinds of perceptions when placed in poetry or lyrics, are accepted as "creative" and "genius," and not crazy talk. Like when Kurt Cobain sang, "I wish I could eat your cancer."

"Word salad" is completely different from just assigning new meanings to words. Word salad is often the sign of advanced schizophrenia or dementia when a person puts words together that make no sense at all and don't abide by normal syntax. For example, someone might say, "I need to use the bathroom, and then we can go for a drive in the car." The word salad version of that could be scrambled in such a way as to come out, "the bathroom car then drive and use to need." I have visited psychiatric hospitals and even some Board and Cares where I tried to have a conversation with another patient, only to be frustrated by their word salad and the severity of their psychosis. With some, I couldn't even make light banter and show some interest in them. People with serious mental illness are some of the loneliest people on the planet. They struggle to make conversation and connections with others, whether they have the word salad problem or not.

When Noah moved to this Board and Care in the Hollywood area in September of 2014, this was the beginning of a serious downward trajectory. In mental health terms, this is sometimes called "decompensating," when a person begins a downward spiral of instability. Sometimes it can start so subtle that most people don't notice, but eventually, it becomes obvious. I could tell by the tone of Noah's voice if he was not yet hypomanic, but when he was on his way. His voice lowers ever so slightly and he speaks slower. Some people do the opposite. They begin to talk faster, with excitability and sometimes incoherence. This is referred to as "pressured speech." I couldn't tell if Noah's decompensation was occurring organically or if his anti-social behaviors were fueled by crystal meth, but he was making it very hard for me to be around him. At this time, Ron decided to no longer accompany me on visits to Noah.

The Hollywood Board and Care is where I saw first-hand regularly the precarious nature of an understaffed facility. The program director would be gone a lot, interviewing new prospective residents in the hospitals, sometimes while his cleaning lady and cook would be the only staff on the premises. The cook did not speak English. One time I was there to visit Noah and I witnessed another resident call 911 on the outside patio. He told the 911 operator he felt like walking into traffic and an ambulance arrived shortly thereafter. The man was put on a gurney and taken away, while the cook and cleaning lady were oblivious inside the building. I went inside to inform them, in my broken Spanish.

Within a couple of months of being at the Hollywood Board and Care, Noah started to urinate in other places besides a toilet. I begged for an explanation, but he was not forthcoming. I was told he was peeing on the floor in his carpeted bedroom. Noah was making excuses about how the bathroom door would get locked at night by accident and he couldn't wait until morning when more staff arrived and opened up the bathroom. Not much was making sense and the bathroom on his second floor was not the only bathroom in the facility. I knew I would have to pay for the carpet to be replaced in his bedroom and after they put in a new carpet, I brought a large bucket for him to use in an emergency, instead of peeing on the newly replaced carpet. Though not a great solution to the problem, I tried to avoid having to pay for more carpet while frantically figuring out what to do. On the one hand, I wanted to rule out a legitimate medical problem. I had read on-line that some anti-psychotics can make even young men incontinent. I also asked the Board and Care owner to help me get my son hospitalized, but he insisted that he didn't meet the criteria and that it was a "behavioral issue" and not psychosis.

This Board and Care owner tried to reason with Noah, but nothing worked. One day, Noah demanded that this Board and Care director give him all his "PNI" money. This was the portion of his disability benefits he was allowed to spend as he pleased. The majority of the benefits paid for his food and rent. Legally, the Board and Care director had to give Noah his PNI (Personal Needs Income).

Normally, the operators dole out the money in small increments twice a week; residents typically have a hard time saving this $130 per month allowance. It was near the beginning of the month, so he gave Noah the remaining $100.00. The first thing he did was to visit a pawnshop and bought a guitar for $70.00. He then spent the rest on lunch and sodas but ran out of money before he could buy himself cigarettes. Noah went back to the pawnshop and asked if he could return the guitar and get his money back. They only offered him $10 and he took it. This is just one of many examples of him making very bad choices and being taken advantage of. Being taken advantage of financially may be the least of our concerns as I've seen surveillance videos of mentally ill homeless people, minding their own business, when a passerby punches them, shoots them, or even sets the innocent person on fire!

The Board and Care owner could tell I was a responsible parent, so he gave Noah a "soft" eviction, meaning Noah had to leave, but he didn't put an exact date on it. The owner knew I was frantically calling around, trying to find other placement for Noah. He told me to take as long as I needed. I guess he felt confident I would pay for all property damages, which I did.

The psychiatrist attending this Board and Care was personable, but also irresponsible. Noah asked him to prescribe a popular ADD medication, which I later found out has the same molecular structure as crystal meth. Even this psychiatrist, Dr. Landmark, said to my face that normally people with schizophrenia should not take medication for Attention Deficit Disorder, as it can propel them into mania. But he made some pact with Noah that he would prescribe it as long as Noah promised not to take crystal meth! Within a couple of weeks, Noah's behavior was even more agitated and Dr. Landmark recognized he made a mistake and took him off of the ADD medication. The cleaning lady told me Noah was snorting his medications in his bedroom, which I learned can produce a high. After that was discovered, he took his medications orally in front of the staff.

Why would Dr. Landmark be so careless with Noah? Sometimes I wonder if current-day psychiatric patients are still being used as blind case studies for derelict medication trials. While not the subject of this book, it should be known that historically, many psychiatric patients have been experimented on without their knowledge or permission. Even I get paranoid about that sometimes. Dr. Landmark put Noah on a medication he knew could cause mania, a medication his colleagues would not have prescribed.

The urinating was upsetting and I took Noah to a nearby Urologist for testing. He did give Noah a prescription for incontinence and the pills made a difference. They might have even made it hard for him to relieve himself. However, Noah didn't want to return to the doctor twelve months later to get a prescription re-fill. I have no idea what went on behind closed doors in the exam room, but I have a feeling the doctor had to do some kind of proctology exam on the first visit; that was probably just too much for Noah to handle.

I was driving Noah to the urologist one morning for the refill office visit, when Noah practically jumped out of the car, saying he refused to see that doctor again. It was then that he told me he didn't need the medication, and that he had been urinating on the floor because he was angry. This was quite disturbing to hear, and it wasn't the last time we had to deal with his urinating in inappropriate places. It was surreal; my child who had been potty-trained easily and never had an "accident" as a little boy was now semi-incontinent at the age of twenty-three.

Aside from his peeing all over the place as an act of rebellion, he also seemed to have an obsessive-compulsive habit that was genuinely making him have an overactive bladder. The more Noah smoked, the more he felt he needed to drink. He'd smoke a cigarette and then reflexively drink something. If not water, then he was guzzling sodas, coffee, or other caffeinated energy drinks. He insisted he needed to drink something each time he had a cigarette and he was smoking forty to sixty cigarettes per day. I couldn't convince him to stop drinking so much, which may have been harmful to his kidneys. When I would take him somewhere, he needed to have me stop every ten minutes at a gas station or a store to use a public bathroom. It was making *me* crazy and I didn't know how to stop his compulsion. Urinating on the floor, and worse, on his roommate's bed one time, were some of the reasons for his continual evictions.

He was also smoking in his bedroom when virtually all of the Board and Cares mandate that smoking is only outside. I tried to explain to Noah he was putting the facility's state license at risk by not abiding by the smoking laws. He didn't care. He also drew on the walls, including semi-pornographic cartoons with references to drugs and drug paraphernalia.

Finding housing for Noah was getting more difficult. Ron was pulling away from both of us and some topics with Ron became off-limits. Ron was now on a course of self-study, deciding he wanted to be an IT specialist (Information Technology). This was a real departure from case management, but he already had an affinity towards all things technological. When he worked in mental health, Ron said he was the go-to guy in the office to fix all the computer problems. With his real Attention Deficit Disorder, Ron moved at a snail's pace studying and reading on his own.

EIGHT:

More Insults to Injury

I found another Board and Care for Noah, despite him being uncommunicative with the Program Director when I took him for an interview. When I called her days later, she said he was a "good boy." Noah does have the ability to make a nice first impression and at times hides his psychosis well. But a few more days after that, she called to say he was doing all kinds of objectionable things, including drawing on the walls and allowing a homeless person to stay in his room for the night.

It is rarely a good sign when the Board and Care calls and because of the many phone calls I received like this one, I developed my own intermittent, phone-specific type of PTSD. To this day, I get tense when the phone rings. No matter where my son is living or the circumstances, I was conditioned to hear bad or shocking news when I answered the phone. Noah was given an eviction notice for this latest Board and Care after two weeks living there. I moved quickly to find him some other housing, but I was running out of choices. I had become so forlorn and pessimistic that I finally broke down and called the L.A. County Department of Mental Health for assistance.

I was aware of a program called FSP, which stands for Full-Service Partnership, begun in 2004 when California voters passed Proposition 63, the Millionaire's tax. This is the proposition that supplies money to the Mental Health Services Act (MHSA). One of the programs, now funded through the MHSA, is the voluntary FSP program. If a person is willing, they receive a therapist, a case manager, and a psychiatrist. One of the services they provide is housing placement leads.

The Department of Mental Health contracts with these FSP programs; they also have one branch called TAY-FSP. TAY stands for Transitional Age Youth and is for young adults between eighteen to twenty-four years old. I told my son I had run out of options in finding him a place to live and we were close to him being homeless. It was for that reason alone he agreed to meet with an FSP representative, but it took some time to set up an initial interview. Before he even had a chance to formally meet with an FSP case manager, Noah was 5150'd and hospitalized days before he was to be evicted. What triggered the Board and Care to call the police was an incident, which could have landed Noah in jail, but fortunately was handled as a mental health issue instead.

Before this incident, I had been asking the Board and Care director to please help me get Noah hospitalized. He was unstable and need a higher level of care. This director refused to help, which now appeared more the norm than the exception. The attending psychiatrist at this facility, Dr. Schnur, was worse than useless. I found out he was nearly 80 years old and definitely from the era when psychiatrists blamed the mother for their child's schizophrenia.

In one conversation I had with him, he said, "all the medications are the same and none of them work very well." This is objectively not true. He also said my son was "hopeless." I chalked it up to the wildly inappropriate things that can come out of the mouths of psychiatrists, harkening back eight years prior when Dr. Harris told us that Noah had a choice between gaining a hundred pounds on medication or be insane.

Months later, after Noah no longer lived at that Board and Care, I noticed that Dr. Schnur was still billing my son's private insurance policy. I called him to question why he was still billing weekly sessions for months after Noah departed that Board and

Care. He had no answer except to say that he would check with his secretary. I ended up filing a complaint with the American Psychiatric Association.

Two years later, the American Psychiatric Association wrote me that what Dr. Schnur did was wrong (insurance fraud), but they would not take his license away or have any disciplinary action because it was the first time a complaint was filed against him. Dr. Schnur worked for at least one other Board and Care in the area. He could have been over-billing the insurance companies for hundreds of visits per month, but this was the first time he was caught. I wondered how many people with mental illness get taken advantage of, without anyone to notice these fraudulent claims.

Some of these Board and Care psychiatrists, having no personal practice, go from one Board and Care to the next, prescribing without even meeting regularly with the patients. Some Board and Care staff will knowingly over-medicate certain residents to keep them docile and compliant. Is it any wonder many overly medicated patients drink huge amounts of coffee to feel alive?

It gets worse. When I researched reviews of a psychiatric hospital online, I saw they were fined when it was discovered a male nurse was raping a female resident in exchange for giving her more cigarettes. Several years prior, my son was hospitalized and I noticed the hospital billed the insurance for a set of x-rays, days after he had been discharged. Imagine how much less all our insurance premiums might be if there was not such rampant fraud within the health care industry!

A week before Noah was 5150'd from the Board and Care, he went missing. The Board and Care director had yelled at my son and told him to get lost. Legally, he still had another couple of weeks to live there, but he took what she said literally and he started walking. I found out about it and called the police. I met up with them in front of the Board and Care to discuss whether or not they would do a "courtesy" search for him, even though it had not been 24 hours since he'd gone missing. That is the usual waiting period before you can call an adult a Missing Person. I brought a photo of Noah in case they would be willing to look for him.

Seven years earlier, when Noah was at the out-of-state residential high school, I had a horrible nightmare where Noah went missing and I was frantically faxing a picture of him to police just before I woke up. Now I was playing out something similar in real life.

The police officer said they were very busy and while we were talking on the curb, he pointed out that the car that just passed us was reported stolen and he needed to get going and pursue the crime in progress. I mentioned that I would start looking for him myself and the officer shook his head as if to say "no." He then told me it was a very bad neighborhood and I shouldn't walk around. When I went inside the Board and Care to speak with the director, she said about my son, "You should take him out to the desert and leave him there." Yes, she said that! This is the same woman who said he as "a good boy" just a few weeks prior. I was so shocked I had no response. Even if she was kidding, what kind of person who works with the mentally ill insults the mother with such insensitivity?

While there, a cleaning lady came into the dining hall where we were and she told me a man outside was looking for Noah. I asked who it was and she said, "I don't know who he is, but he says he wants to kill your son." Wow. These are the kinds of "delightful" things one can encounter when dealing with a Board and Care that operates in a bad neighborhood with uncaring, indifferent staff operating on automatic pilot.

Most residents have too much time on their hands since little or no services are extended to them. This particular Board and Care was on a busy street but with only about fifteen residents, much smaller than most. It was also devoid of any kind of recreational room or facilities. Just bedrooms and bathrooms upstairs, it had a commercial kitchen and dining room downstairs. Most Board and Cares are furnished with the type of bedroom and living room furniture you would expect to see at Good Will or worse. The single beds are not very comfortable, with older box springs and mattresses. Dresser drawers may not open easily and views out the window may be a busy street, an alley, or the side of another building. Lights are dim; the walls a dull beige or yellow. A small separate structure on the property was the office space for the Board and Care director. They stored kitchen supplies here and the visiting psychiatrist would meet with people if the Doctor even showed up at all.

Whether or not a Board and Care provides lounge space for the residents, many of them stay isolated in their bedrooms. There might be a blaring TV that hardly anyone watches or none at all. Some who are less self-isolating, roam around the neighborhood, frequenting the fast-food restaurants, meandering around the discount stores, mini-markets, and liquor stores. Some will attract, like a magnet, the local drug dealer where they can purchase small quantities of anything you can imagine. Some neighborhoods and vendors have a higher tolerance for panhandling than others. This is one reason why they start taking street drugs: to relieve boredom and to escape their reality. The only people who have more variety in their schedules are those who have family members visiting them, taking them out to eat or those who have been assigned a therapist and case manager. Sometimes, all the case manager or therapist can do is help the person get certain mundane things accomplished, like getting a bus pass, a DMV ID renewal, a trip to a doctor, or the Social Security Administration.

It should also be noted that antipsychotic medications can have unpleasant side-effects. You have to ask yourself if you would be willing to take medications you didn't think you needed if they did any of the following as a bonus:

- Make you sleep 12+ hours a day
- Make you ravenously hungry all the time
- Make it hard to focus on anything
- Cause erectile dysfunction or other sexual problems
- Make you shake or twitch like you have Parkinson's disease

There are more serious, even life-threatening side effects as well. Studies have shown that people who are prescribed medications for physical ailments (not psychiatric), only comply about 50% of the time. Many of us are also guilty of not following doctor's orders.

I did hear from my son on the day the director told him to get lost. He was walking around miles away between the Board and Care and my home. A stranger let him use their cell phone to call me. I picked him up and brought him right back to the Board and Care. I had spent the earlier part of the day trying to arrange for a mobile psychiatric team to evaluate him. These mobile psych teams go by various acronyms, such as PET, CAT, or SMART teams. A person has to be reliably in a certain location before the PET Team or the SMART Team will commit to coming out. They can't go looking for a missing person and I understand that. I asked the one man on staff at the Board and Care that night to watch my son and keep him on the premises. When the mobile psych team was almost there, they called me so I could arrive at the same time. They had two police cars accompany them based on what I told them over the phone earlier in the day. The PET team felt they would probably 5150 him. Police are called as back up in case the person resists or becomes violent.

True to form, Noah acted quiet and calm when the PET TEAM social workers interviewed him outside the Board and Care. He answered questions appropriately and presented, as he has before like he did not need emergency care. I asked the social workers to go into his bedroom to have a look at the drawings on the wall. The drawings included lists of drugs he wanted to take and pornographic cartoons. There were no threats of violence, however.

One common frustration for many parents is the difficulty in getting the mobile psych team to authorize a 5150 hold. For reasons which we can't understand, our mentally ill loved one, even when they are psychotic, can fool the professionals a high percentage of the time. Somehow, they can pull it together even when moments before they were acting out in a way that would concern and scare anyone. I once asked a program director at another Board and Care how this is even possible, and his response was, "They may be crazy, but they are not stupid." I guess he was implying that even in a state of debilitating psychosis, an otherwise intelligent person recognizes that they better act "normal" if they don't want to be taken against their will to a hospital. Of course, there are many instances when the ill person cannot "fake" it. If they are naked and howling at the moon, then the PET team will get the person hospitalized, but only if there is a bed available! Worse, it's the people who respond aggressively to police who sometimes end up dead.

In this instance, the mobile psych team consisted of two young women who were not much older than my son. I now classify them in the group of mental health practitioners who were inexperienced, surprisingly naïve, and more concerned with protecting the perceived rights of a psychotic person than they were in getting someone the help they needed.

After fifteen minutes of interviewing Noah, they decided he did not fit the criteria for a 72-hour hold. I was livid, as I had spent the majority of the day looking for him, arranging for the mobile psych team to come, speaking with the local police, and being on the receiving end of the Board and Care director's insults. As the women were returning to their car and the police were leaving, I walked over to these young female social workers and told them that they had made a mistake in not authorizing the 72-hour hold (5150). They looked at me smugly and said I could call them again the next day if more problems arose. At this point, I also regretted insisting that Noah clean himself up and change his clothes before their arrival to evaluate him. When I had picked him up hours earlier, he stunk to high heaven. He smelled like a mixture of sweat, urine, and shit. I almost gagged when he got in the car and he promptly told me that he resorted to using bushes (and his hands) to relieve himself that day. Call it mother's pride but I just didn't want him to smell so horrible when the social workers talked to him. In retrospect, just his odor alone could have been a compelling piece of evidence he was in fact, "gravely ill." My advice to parents is to let your son or daughter be as filthy as possible when they are about to be evaluated for a 5150. As soon as they left, my son gave me a bizarre look of defiance and he started acting out again. Now I had to wait for another, more compelling incident. It came a week later.

NINE:

More Drama

I picked up the phone a week later and a female police officer identified herself and quickly told me my son was okay and she was taking him to their precinct for evaluation. She asked me if the Board and Care told me what happened and I said no. The Board and Care director who told me I should dump my son off in the desert had not informed me that she had called the police.

Noah had exposed himself to one of the cleaning ladies. He also allegedly chased her around the Board and Care with a knife. I was so stunned. I said to the police officer, "What, like a plastic knife from Taco Bell?" I could not even fathom my son running around the facility, threatening anyone with an actual metal knife.

He ended up in the hospital for two months, after having to wait in the Emergency Room for five days. While I was appalled at the situation, the reason he was stuck for five days in the ER was for the usual reasons other families encounter as well; there is an obscene lack of psychiatric beds available. Many have shut down their psychiatric units over the decades leaving many psychiatric facilities in this country that still stand empty and never repurposed. Most communities in the U.S. have about 10% of the psychiatric beds they used to. That leaves us with home care, the streets, or prison.

Many people are vaguely aware of this decades-long crisis and blame President Ronald Reagan for mandating the closure of many state hospitals in the 1980s. But the problem began more than a decade earlier. Dr. E. Fuller Torrey, in his book, *American Psychosis*, explains in detail how the last piece of legislation President John F. Kennedy signed in 1963 before he was assassinated, paved the way for state mental hospitals to close. The federal government planned to take over with federally funded outpatient, community mental health care clinics. Those involved at the time, including a young Dr. Torrey, admitted they had no evidence seriously mentally ill people would voluntarily seek out mental health care services or even be able to survive on their own.

As decades passed, results were predictable. The direct correlation between the increase in homelessness and incarceration of the seriously mentally ill could not be denied. Our society, in the name of giving people the right to be psychotic and not treated against their will, had criminalized a genetically based neurological brain illness. One time, my local NAMI chapter organized a fruitless protest in front of a local Medical Center as they were closing their psychiatric wing. They turned it into a cancer unit that would surely bring in a lot more money than beds for those with mental illness.

Another reason why Noah waited five days in the Emergency Room was because of insurance. At the time of this writing, California's Medi-Cal and nation-wide Medicaid does not cover psychiatric hospital stays. It's called the IMD Exclusion clause. IMD stands for the Institute of Mental Disease, which includes the ever-diminishing psychiatric wards at all hospitals. This happened right when I dropped Noah's private insurance so that he could participate in outpatient programs such as the FSP (Full Service Partnership) which is eligible to those with Medi-Cal coverage. I don't know how they come up with these names; I suppose the "partnership" is between the mental health care providers and the patient.

The ER nurse told me that one nearby hospital had a bed, but didn't want to take Noah because his private insurance was ending just days later. There was also incompetence on the part of the ER staff when it came to evaluating Noah. Trying to get any information at all out of them was difficult because of HIPAA privacy laws that discriminate against family members of a mentally ill adult, another grotesque example of how privacy laws violate their usefulness.

This is one of the more perverse parts of the Mental Illness Industrial Complex. Not having good judgment or the legal ability to speak with me, the ER staff delayed finding an appropriate placement. A nurse made a comment to me over the phone which let me know they assumed Noah was developmentally disabled. These people were clueless. Examples of developmental disabilities include autism, behavior disorders, brain injury, cerebral palsy, Down syndrome, fetal alcohol syndrome, intellectual disability, and spina bifida. If that were the case, a completely different type of care would have been necessary for Noah. I held my tongue from saying to the nurse that Noah probably had a higher IQ than she did and he had schizophrenia, not mental retardation! So many mistakes could be avoided if mental health care workers made a small effort to talk to the family members! HIPAA Privacy Laws have caused more incorrect diagnoses and inappropriate treatments than can even be imagined. More than once I have called a hospital to find out if my son had been admitted there and they refused to confirm or deny it. The "rules" range from silly to sadistic.

This was 2015 and once he was hospitalized, the social worker in charge called me to say he wasn't sure if Noah had a mental illness. So, in two weeks, a psychiatric nurse and a psychiatric social worker were not able to recognize schizophrenia!

He thought the odd behaviors, the aggressiveness, and anti-social incident were perhaps just drug-induced as if he just partied too hard at a Lollapalooza festival. I was stunned by this speculation; a half-dozen psychiatrists had already diagnosed Noah. There was previously never any doubt that Noah was seriously mentally ill, yet, when a parent hears a mental health professional give their opinion, we tend to listen most of the time.

This hospital social worker did make a point of telling both me and Noah's father how lucky we were that the indecent exposure incident was handled as a mental health problem, as opposed to sending Noah to county jail. In a vivid, memorable way, he described the behaviors of the inmates at L.A. County jail as being like "gladiators." Noah would have probably been beaten to a pulp there. I didn't say much in response to this one social worker's opinion; it would not be the first time the professionals in charge came to a wrong conclusion or diagnosis.

As a case in point, I have a friend whose son disputed the renewal of his conservatorship. When this happens, a conserved person is granted free legal counsel. They can have an attorney, a Public Defender, represent their interests or they can represent themselves. When a person is conserved, another adult takes over as their Legal Guardian and they can make important decisions on their behalf, such as where the conserved person lives and what medications they take.

This one young man, Steve, showed up at court wearing a three-piece suit his father loaned him so that he would not appear before the judge looking like a disheveled wreck. The facility he was living at had a representative tell the judge in Mental Health court that Steve was *not* stable, but the judge ignored this input without explanation. Further, the mother had the treating psychiatrist present at the court hearing to also say her son was *not* stable and should remain conserved by her. This young man was telling people he had a family on the moon, but he didn't say that to the judge. His conservatorship was not renewed because the judge thought he presented well in court and looked sharp in his three-piece suit.

Steve also lied to the judge that he wanted to one day open a healing center and that he had the financial means to support himself. Once again, an unstable man who still needed to be conserved managed to fool a Mental Health Court judge into believing he did not need protective legal conservatorship continued for another year. She defied the recommendations of the caregivers as well. This young, delusional man also told the judge that he wanted to heal himself naturally with something called "ayahuasca." The judge didn't know what that was apparently. Ayahuasca is a very strong hallucinogen!

My friend became despondent over the judge's mishandling of the case who terminated the conservatorship she had with her son. Keep in mind these cases are held in "Mental Health Court" as distinct from other courts. The judges, even if new to their position, should be briefed enough that they should think twice about terminating a conservatorship when the person's psychiatrist shows up in court to say a person still needs to be conserved!

With the conservatorship canceled, this mother had to go on anti-depressants to not lose her mind. In less than a year, my friend's son was isolating by himself in an apartment paid for by mom. He refused treatment or medication because legally he no longer had to comply since the conservatorship ended. He rapidly decompensated and it was only a matter of time before he would be hospitalized again or something worse. All of this could have been avoided had the judge allowed the conservatorship to be renewed. It should also be stated, that each time a person goes off their medication and becomes psychotic, it gets harder and harder to bring the person back to stability.

During Noah's 2015 hospitalization, the prospect of getting him conserved was quickly rejected by the hospital Powers That Be, and yet he stayed at the hospital for two months. They had a very hard time placing him, as no Board and Care would take a person who had been violent or threatening. This was exactly why he needed a higher level of care. During his long stay, they ordered a comprehensive evaluation of Noah, even though I did not request it. Dr. Canyon produced a thirteen-page report from several days of testing. She concluded he was seriously mentally ill, with schizophrenia, but also with a secondary diagnosis of poly-substance abuse disorder. She recommended he be in a highly supervised and structured environment. She also placed his cognitive abilities well behind his actual chronological age. She thought he might need to be in a locked facility (IMD) for some time.

So much for the psych ward social worker that questioned whether or not Noah was even mentally ill. I guess he thought my son was just a drug addict, even though he entered the hospital with no illicit drugs in his bloodstream. This is just one of many exasperating examples of how family members are misinformed and misdirected. Often the ill person's recovery is seriously delayed or even sabotaged by either poorly trained or overworked health care providers. According to a study by John Hopkins, over a quarter of a million U.S. citizens die each year due to medical malpractice, making it the third leading cause of death after cancer and heart disease. I can only speculate how much malpractice occurs in the psychiatric field. Within my NAMI family support group, I know of several men with schizophrenia, who died unnecessarily because of negligence or bureaucratic blunders.

I was grateful for the report by Dr. Canyon and I shared it with as many mental health professionals as I could in future placement scenarios. A highly explicit professional evaluation, this report validated my son's struggles and what he needed in terms of optimal care. In one section of Dr. Canyon's testing, Noah was asked to interpret an illustration of a woman standing at a kitchen sink filled with dishes and overflowing water. Behind the woman was a ladder falling toward her. All Noah could say was, "something's gone awry." In another part of the test, Noah was asked what he would do if he saw a baby, all by itself, crawling on an ocean pier. Noah only said, "I would have nothing to do with that." The only answer Noah gave, which made me smile a little, was to a question about what he would do if he was stranded at an airport with only a couple of quarters in his pocket. He replied that he would offer someone the quarters in exchange for two cigarettes and then find someone to let him borrow their phone. We could question his priorities, but at least he knew how to be resourceful and get his needs met.

The mental health experts no longer had to humor a pushy mother. They could refer to a report written by an authority, one of their peers. But what Dr. Canyon recommended was not implemented. Instead, the same hospital was on the verge of discharging Noah with a bus token and the address to a local homeless shelter. This is the same hospital that ordered the evaluation yet had no intention of following the recommendations! At the 11th hour, there was just one Board and Care director willing to interview Noah. Beggars can't be choosers, so I bribed my son to stay in the hospital one more day so that this person could accept him to his Board and Care. Noah was antsy to leave the hospital, understandably. That said, he didn't see the wisdom in staying one more day for the chance to have a place to live, instead of being released the streets.

Family support coaches recommend to parents that they tell the discharge nurse their relative may *not* come home with them. The goal is to make the discharge nurse work harder at finding a placement and an appropriate level of care. It doesn't always work out in favor of the patient. Often, we have what is called "patient dumping" with the mentally ill. Since I visited Noah in the hospital, maybe the staff assumed I would not allow Noah to be homeless if they just discharged him with a bus token.

My son agreed to stay in the hospital one more day to be interviewed in exchange for a McDonald's Happy Meal. That was one easy request to fill. Noah presented well for the interview, downplayed what happened in his own words, and was able to move into yet another Board and Care. This place was possibly the worst of the worst. He ended up with a roommate who was in his fifties, a chronically ill man, who also shot up heroin in the bedroom in front of Noah. Additionally, there was a resident at the Board and Care who "hired" my son to deliver or pick up crystal meth in exchange for getting some free meth for himself. I kept urging Noah to play by the rules and not cause property damage. He had already broken a window and a dresser shortly after moving in. I consistently told him that if he can demonstrate responsible behavior, he would eventually live in a place he likes. He just couldn't understand those words or promises. In my mind, the possibility of him ever living well on his own got more and more remote.

One day he left the Board and Care and they didn't notice him missing until the following morning during medication management. By this time, he did have an FSP team visiting him weekly. While Noah had been in the hospital for two months, the FSP team was on hold. But the therapist and case manager began to work with him as soon as he was discharged from the hospital. The therapist had already urged him to try harder to remain in good standing at this facility. But she could see the writing on the wall, almost literally in the case of Noah, and knew he would probably not do well at *any* Board and Care. Even while Noah was missing, she decided he had to be placed somewhere else.

A day later Noah called me, just like he had done months before, wanting to be picked up. Each time he would go missing, I would hope that he had some kind of epiphany or experience that would give him pause not to do such a thing again. That never happened. Instead, he had had a fairly good time wandering around the good and bad parts of Los Angeles. People had given him water, sodas, and food. When I met him outside the bank where he said he would be that night, I found him in the middle of a conversation with an elderly man who was giving him some loose tobacco for his pipe. Noah had had a nice little adventure, at the expense of everyone else in a panic about where he was. On the drive back to the Board and Care, we called his therapist. She asked him a series of questions to determine if he should be hospitalized and she said he didn't fit the criteria. She asked why he left the Board and Care and Noah told her he didn't like the cleaning lady telling him to clean up his room. The next day began yet another search to find him better housing than the typical Board and Care.

Weeks later, she came up with a place that focused on helping previously homeless or incarcerated men find permanent housing and jobs. Many of the men were recovering from addiction and they had weekly 12-Step meetings right at the house. I suppose some suffered from mental illness, but they were all much higher functioning than Noah. Some of the men were even married and they could spend the weekend with their families. In this household, Noah was the "baby" in the group. He was the one who stayed home all day while the other men were meeting with prospective employers and probation officers.

The man who directed this household was both imposing and very patient. He probably weighed over 300 pounds and Noah was intimidated. He was an African-American man who joined Islam after the 1992 L.A. riots and had worked in many capacities as a guide or counselor to troubled people. He didn't have a lot of experience with mental illness, however. He kept telling the other men in the household to be patient with Noah and to be glad they didn't have his problems.

Noah tested everyone's patience at this household and he may not have understood he was living with former gang members who could cause serious harm if he disrespected them. The program director told me confidentially, he instructed all the men to deal with him directly if they had an issue with Noah.

This was somewhat ironic given that one of Noah's very first paranoid delusions had to do with being surrounded by the Crips and the Bloods at his high school. Now he was sharing a house with some of them but was seemingly oblivious to it.

Noah pushed their buttons in several ways, from eating other people's food to passing gas in his roommate's face, I later learned. If I had been a fly on the wall in that house, I don't know if I would have been amused or terrified by the interactions going on between the other men and my son.

The program director was a compassionate drill sergeant. He got Noah to do all kinds of cleaning chores and follow all the house rules. Part of the command he had over Noah was because he lived in the house. The program director was more often than not, just ten to twenty feet away from Noah, monitoring his every move. The one area where they had little control was how much smoking Noah managed to squeeze in each day. They told me Noah once coughed so hard, he fell out of the patio chair. Another time he coughed so hard, he threw up his meal. Even the neighbors were concerned with his coughing induced from all the smoking, as it sounded like someone required serious medical attention.

During his six-month stay, I was impressed with Noah's compliance. They even got him to wash his stinky feet twice a day, changing his socks each time and using foot deodorant. But Noah didn't like it there and asked to move again. His therapist and case manager didn't want Noah to think they were only at his beck and call to find him housing but agreed to find him another place if he promised to live there for at least a year.

TEN:

Starring in a Movie I Don't Want to Be In

In a couple of months, the FSP therapist and case manager found Noah a Dual Diagnosis residence he could move into. This was a new type of housing we had not tried before. It seemed like the most appropriate level of care in that they catered to *both* mental illness and drug addiction. In March of 2016, Noah moved there, and I felt somewhat hopeful as to how they could help him. What I quickly realized after he moved in was that there were no special services provided for men with Dual Diagnosis. It was just another board and care, but unlicensed. Like the previous household that was also not a state-licensed facility, only a portion of meals was provided and the majority of the residents were gone during the day. All of the men except Noah participated in mental health programs off-site where they provided lunch. A few men had an actual job to go to.

Noah was home when others were out. I needed to supplement him with more meals than he was offered. I grocery shopped for him and tried to make it easy. I picked up frozen meals with the least amount of processed ingredients and freshly prepared salads. At one point, Noah asked me to stop bringing the salads. It wasn't because he didn't like salads; his reason was he "didn't like the way the plastic fork sounded when it scratched the bottom of the plastic bowl." For highly sensitive people, this might be bothersome enough to use another fork or bowl. For my son, it was reason enough to not want the salads anymore.

The program director at this Dual Diagnosis house was a young man, not much older than Noah. He had only been out of jail and sober for two years, I later learned. This was a typical scenario, where a person either feels like "giving back" for the help they received when down and out, or it could be a court-ordered job, working as a program director in a group home. I had asked him to dole out Noah's PNI spending money and cigarettes, but there was much manipulation going on, driven by Noah, right from the start. This young man, who was trying to direct Noah positively, was struggling with Noah's non-compliance and confrontational gestures. After doing every type of cleaning imaginable at the previous house, from vacuuming and dusting to cleaning toilets, Noah behaved as if he was helpless and reluctant to do any household chores at this Dual Diagnosis center. Not to make excuses for my son, I do know that when he first moved in, he was given the impression he would have certain tasks to complete and no more.

One day when the household of men was asked to do a big landscaping clean-up project, Noah didn't think he needed to help because he was not explicitly forewarned spontaneous group projects would ever be required of him. People with serious mental illness do not always respond well to sudden requests by others or changes in schedule. Somehow, it's okay for Noah to change his mind constantly, but when asked to deviate from his schedule by others, it causes tremendous resistance. People with schizophrenia do much better with the structure of a consistent, anticipated routine. Once "mastered," they can be asked to do more.

The House Manager called me one day, actually crying, because he was afraid he was going to get in trouble with the owner of the Dual Diagnosis Center, and it was partly Noah's fault. Donny told me Noah became irate because he would not give Noah more cigarettes than what I had instructed him to give. Noah was also disputing the amount of money I asked

Donny to give him weekly. Noah ended up calling 911 because he felt it was his legal right to have all his money and his cigarettes. When the police arrived, they didn't take too kindly to the fact my son was wasting their time with such a frivolous matter. Donny told me one of the officers asked Noah, "Who pays for the cigarettes?" and Noah said it was his mother. The police told Noah he had to abide by my cigarette schedule. And they told Noah that if he called 911 again for a non-emergency, they would arrest HIM!

Donny the House Manager was quite upset the police were called, but I tried to make him feel better by pointing out this could have been a "teachable moment" for Noah. The owner of the Dual Diagnosis Center got pissed off because she found out the police were called. Like other Sober Living houses and Board and Cares, operators cannot weather too many complaints from neighbors if they want to continue with group homes in residential settings. While this complaint did not come from a neighbor, group home operators do not want any stigma associated with their residences. With NIMBY-ism (Not in My Backyard) a real issue, the owner did not want neighbors to see the police show up, for any reason, at her residential program. As a result, the next day she evicted Noah. She also fired the House Manager, Donny.

This was a new type of eviction because she did not even give Noah a 30-day notice, or a week's notice, or even a few days' notice. He had to pack his things and be out immediately; so much for compassionate mental healthcare providers.

In retrospect, I could have pointed out her actions were probably illegal. But I made a split decision to not dispute the immediate eviction. In the small world of Board and Cares, once again I did not want my son "blacklisted" or have his name passed around as someone never to rent to; some of these Board and Cares are extended family businesses. I am willing to bet many of them know each other, as they shuffle around the same clients from one place to the next.

Noah's therapist and case manager did not try to get the owner to calm down and let Noah stay, at least until they found a new place for him. I believe they should have found him emergency housing, but they were also at their wits' end because Noah had promised he would stay in one place for at least a year. This eviction was coming just two months later. On top of that, we always seemed to have an emergency with Noah at a time when one or both of his FSP team were on vacation or otherwise indisposed. Noah did not plan on having a crisis when they were unavailable, but he didn't seem to care one way or another if they helped him or not. Noah assumed mom would come to the rescue and this was partially true.

I remember clearly his therapist Marianne said she could not be of any immediate help because she had her hands full with a young troubled pre-teen whose father had just been killed the night before. She said, to me, her maternal instincts decided to prioritize the little girl over Noah's sudden eviction. I was beyond burn-out myself and could not understand why a substitute therapist from the FSP program could not be counted on to do her job. Why should a client like Noah be left hanging during a crisis? Why would anyone, no less a "professional," refuse to help a patient as sick as Noah?

I tried to figure something out as quickly as possible but thought it might be appropriate consequences for Noah to stay outdoors for twenty-four hours. He had been tempting homelessness and now he would get a taste of it. Noah ended up going down to a local mini-market a few blocks away. There was an outside phone and a big city streetlight out front and he huddled in the parking lot for thirty-six hours. He stayed near the payphone and I told him I was working on the situation. At this point, he was not complaining. He could panhandle somewhat under the radar and get food at the mini-market and probably a bathroom to use.

This is another example of how I as a parent was constantly struggling with just how much I should allow my ill son to experience the consequences of his actions. This is always a source of tremendous guilt and shame for me; that I won't even take my son into my home, as other parents do, even when their safety may be in danger. I was never really worried about Noah being violent toward me, but I have worried he could cause property damage or compromise the security of my house by leaving doors unlocked or inviting strangers over. I was also afraid he would forget to close doors and my pets would wander off, not to mention that it is just extremely nerve-racking to have an unstable person in the house.

There were brief periods when Noah stayed with me, such as in 2010 when he was in between Sober Living houses for three weeks. Whenever my son was with me, he always wanted to be taken somewhere, like a book or music store, in the middle of the day while I needed to work at home on the computer. I had no problem with short breaks but I would drive him somewhere for an hour and he would only want to stay for ten minutes. Outings to museums or amusement parks eventually stopped because it was too frustrating to spend money in a place neither of us could enjoy in such a short time.

When Noah came to visit at my house for a few hours, it was aggravating to witness a repetitive circuit he put himself on: go outside to smoke, come back in to open the refrigerator, have something to drink, go to the bathroom, and start that routine all over again like a rat on a wheel. Hearing the doors opening and closing continuously put me on edge and I could not concentrate on my work.

In retrospect, I think Ron was worried Noah would end up living with us, especially during these crises. He never demanded

I not allow Noah to live in my own house, but he must have wondered if it would happen eventually. I now recognize that despite Ron's professional experience working with the mentally ill, his post-traumatic stress disorder, anxiety, and depression would have gone off the deep end if Noah was a constant presence in the house. Perhaps I would have as well.

Immediately after Noah got thrown out of the Dual Diagnosis center, I tried to contact several agencies to get him a place to stay, but nothing was working out, so I booked a room at a motel near my house and took him there. I'd love to have all the money back that I wasted on motels, but I couldn't have him at my house during such an unstable time. To add insult to injury, when I went by the Dual Diagnosis center to pick up Noah's clothing and other belongings, the men living there had already stolen Noah's possessions to divide up among themselves. A couple of men agreed to return some of the things they had taken.

As soon as I got him into this motel near my house, the FSP team told me it was located "outside their service area" (by about 10 miles) and that he would have to be moved back to their area to check in on him. This punishing policy is in the process of being reconsidered as I write this. The Department of Mental Health is starting to understand how precarious it is to drop a client or maintain these barriers to care when a person lands in a different part of the city from where they first started with an FSP team. Transiency is so common with this population, it makes no sense that each time a person moves within the city or county, they need to start over with a new care team.

Within a few days, the FSP office called to say they had a motel for him in their service area, which happened to be in a neighborhood with a lot more crime than my part of town. But they had the funds to pay for him to stay a couple of weeks in this motel. Because the therapist was now at a seminar and the case manager on vacation, I felt like it was up to me to find Noah permanent housing once again. I don't even recall being told the exact date when his therapist or case manager would be available again. This frustrating situation deserves its own chapter; the underfunded, unorganized, barely functioning health care system. Funds that should be spent to help the seriously mentally ill are being used for other government programs that taxpayers never intended. This is money that is supposed to be reserved for the most disabled, not for anti-poverty or anti-bullying campaigns. The mental health care system has widened its net so much, they are spending funds (which should be dedicated to the most disabled), on people who are *not* seriously mentally ill and who have other resources such as educational funding and through economic development initiatives.

What may shock the general public is there is an anti-stigma campaign promoted from within the mental health care community which is seriously misguided, if not flatly untrue, and politicized. Many mental health care advocates support a narrative that mentally ill people are no more violent than the rest of the population, a statement contrary to every fact we have. The operative word here is "untreated" mental illness. The UN-treated mentally ill are three times more likely to be violent than the general population (or those who are stable in treatment). Perhaps if more people understood this, we taxpayers would demand those seriously mentally ill people be moved to the front of the line when it comes to mental health care. Without exaggeration, individuals having bad hair days gain access to mental health services easier than the schizophrenic laying in the gutter. If someone opposes the way the mentally ill are treated by law enforcement, just know the police have unfortunately been forced to become first responders, instead of mental health professionals. Not all, but many in the mental health care business, have turned their backs on the most seriously ill and made it clear they have other priorities.

Noah ended up staying at the motel for a month, but not without several warnings. One day when I came to visit and give him money for food, the motel owner told me that Noah had invited a homeless man into his room and of course that was not allowed. I felt that familiar humiliation. It is so ironic, how Noah hadn't had a true friend in many years, but he could somehow trust a stranger from the park to spend the night in his motel room. My guess is drugs were offered in exchange. When I went into his motel room I also saw condoms on the floor. My heart sank. What the hell had gone on in this motel room? Had they invited a hooker into the room? Had my son participated? I even asked incredulously if Noah had sex with this other young man. To that, Noah replied in a monotone, "No, I'm not into guys." Neither would he tell me who used the condoms.

Noah's father was putting twenty dollars per day on a debit card so that Noah could eat out at either the nearby Mexican restaurant or go get food and snacks at the mini-market across the street. Noah having balanced meals was not a priority at this time. His compulsive behaviors were so constant, his father had to put just ten dollars on the card in the morning and another ten dollars on the debit card later in the day. Otherwise, Noah would use up all the money in the morning and then complain he was hungry and needed more by the afternoon.

While it is common for many parents to feel like they are nothing more than ATM machines for their children, having an adult child with mental illness who is a spendthrift produces a special kind of frustration that only other parents in the same club can understand.

It was now June of 2016 and I managed to find a Board and Care with a vacancy and this one was not in a crime-ridden neighborhood. It was in West Hollywood, straddling the seedy main boulevards, but on the same block as million-dollar homes. This new Board and Care operator told me she had a zero-tolerance for bad behavior, so we were forewarned. I brought Noah over there for an interview; he didn't smile or act particularly friendly. We lied in response to some of the questions about why he needed to find a new place to live and muddled through it with enough feigned innocence they agreed to let him live there. It was almost a year previous that his therapist Marianne concluded he would never do well in a typical Board and Care, and yet the therapist did not appear to be helping at all at this moment. I had limited resources in terms of knowing what all options might be available, such as Crisis Residential programs.

Within eleven days, Noah got an eviction notice. He was not showing up for medication management and staff had to chase after him to take his medications. He decided he would not eat the food provided at the Board and Care and so by real necessity, Noah was panhandling like crazy so he could take himself out to eat. I had given him what would be the last of several cell phones, but he sold it or lost it within twelve hours. I did not find out about the eviction notice for a full week. They gave Noah a written notice that he threw away. That was precious time I could have used to find another place for him. They followed through on the eviction a couple of days early. I found out when I got a call one night from a West Hollywood police officer. He had been called to the Board and Care because Noah was trying to get back inside after they had booted him out. He was climbing the fence to get back in and was now accused of trespassing.

Each time Noah would get evicted like this, he would throw away or leave all his clothes and belongings behind. He could not see himself lugging any possessions around with him, the way you see some homeless people with backpacks and shopping carts. Noah tried to jump over the security gate enclosing the Board and Care and that is when they called the police. I know the officer was

Ten: Starring in a Movie I Don't Want to Be In   113

bewildered as to why Noah would instruct him to call me, only to hear me say he can spend the night outdoors. I told the officer that it's a very long story with many evictions. I told him I didn't expect him to understand the situation or why a mom would appear so heartless as to not come to get her son. I continued to get a raised eyebrow from Ron, who felt I had been so lenient with Noah for so many years, I had essentially created this drama myself by not nipping it in the bud years before.

I told Noah through the police officer that he can walk a few blocks down Sunset Boulevard to a Homeless Check-In Center where he could get some food; maybe they could even tell him where to go for shelter. He had survived being outdoors all night just six weeks earlier; he could do it again if he had to.

Around this time, I asked Ron how soon he would be able to take the IT exams, to get certified and possibly join one of the tech firms in the area. Ron admitted to me he was too anxious. I asked Ron how he could imagine himself working with stressed-out clients, anxious for their computer or cell phone to be repaired if he was feeling too anxious to take the certification tests. He turned white in the face and mumbled that he didn't know. My intention was not meant to burst his bubble, but I know for myself that when my technology is not working or my computer has crashed, I'm not fun to be around. I sincerely wondered if he could handle the stress of impatient clients wanting him to fix things immediately.

The next day Ron filed for social security disability. Perhaps I only verbalized what he had been dreading all along. He now admitted to me and himself he was unable to work, consumed with anxiety and depression. He also had severe physical limitations, due to his unrelenting neck and back pain. Surely he would be granted SSDI (Social Security Disability Insurance) for both physical and psychological reasons. We both knew it could be a long wait. It can take several years to get approval and some people are too intimidated to appeal the process if they are initially denied. I tried to comfort Ron by saying I would make sure he got approved for SSDI even if I needed to hire a lawyer on his behalf.

SSDI is disability coverage for people with a work history. SSI (Supplemental Security Income) is for those with disabilities who have never worked, like Noah. In some circumstances, some individuals can qualify for both.

ELEVEN:

Skid Row

After speaking with the West Hollywood police officer and asking him to tell Noah to head for the nearby Drop-In Center, Noah ended up at my doorstep the following morning. Someone from the Drop-In Center had driven Noah to my house. We didn't have a long conversation. He was filthy looking and smelled bad. I gave him a few dollars and told him to get on the bus and go back to the Drop-In Center and ask them how to get to a shelter. I didn't know if he was capable of doing this, but I decided to test it out. Of course, many teens and young adults never make it to a shelter; some stay out all night. Some may find abandoned houses or buildings to escape into. I was so exhausted from finding him places to live that I just wanted him to own some responsibility for the reality as to how and why he was in this position. I figured if he had to seek out his housing, maybe he would value the next place he landed enough to not sabotage it. I have no idea what he did on many occasions, except stay up all night, sitting on the curb smoking. I have also stayed up all night on many occasions, wondering if I had allowed something horrible to happen to him. My active imagination wanders into the darkest places and I fear the worst, like him being kidnapped into human trafficking. If Noah was a daughter instead of a son, I don't know what I would have done; the threat of predators doubled or tripled.

Another few days passed. This time, I got a phone call from Noah. He was being released from a nearby hospital. What happened? He had walked around so much he had blisters on his feet.

He couldn't walk upright and probably look crippled or injured. Someone always lets him use their cell phone and this time he called 911 to say he needed to go to the hospital. From what I gathered, he was at the hospital for less than twenty-four hours. They gave him some clean clothes, bandaged up his feet, gave him antibiotics in case of infection, and a full month's prescription of his medication (which he promptly threw away.) Years earlier I insisted Noah memorize his social security number since he could not reliably protect or keep it in a wallet. He did memorize the numbers and this must be how the hospital identified him in their computer system. They could verify his Medi-Cal coverage and medical history online.

The hospital also gave him the name and phone number of a homeless shelter downtown. When I called that number and looked it up on-line, it had closed five years ago, another example of how patients and caretakers are given the "run around." We are given contact information that goes nowhere: disconnected numbers, closed agencies, or agencies that don't perform the service we need. Around the same time, I called an emergency Homeless referral service. They returned my call *three* months later: So much for emergency help!

Noah tried to find the closed shelter by taking a bus and now he was just back to wandering around a bad section of town. He gave me the cross streets and I picked him up. Before I left, I scoured the internet for homeless shelters to see if they had beds available. It was a Sunday night and most had already closed for the evening and not answering the phones. There was just one shelter that picked up the phone; it was the Union Rescue Mission on Skid Row. The shelter told me that technically, they did not have a bed available, but if we could arrive before 8 p.m., someone who had a cot reserved might fail to show up. I picked up Noah at the corner where he said he would be. One of the more oddly reliable abilities I shared with Noah over the years was that no matter how psychotic or desperate a situation was, picking him up was easy. He could articulate where he was by looking at street signs and was waiting for me every time. We got down to the shelter and it was surprisingly "wholesome" on the inside compared to the absolute circus going on outside. As it turned out, someone did not claim their cot and Noah could sleep there for the night. The next day, he would need to stand in line and officially register for a two-week cot reservation.

I came back to help him register and it took about thirty minutes. We got Noah registered by a man in a wheelchair named John who was there "to do the Lord's work" and he was very personable. John called me for a hand-out months later. He was no longer living or volunteering at Union Rescue Mission. I wired him a hundred dollars and felt like of all people, I should be generous with John.

During Noah's brief time at Union Rescue Mission, where John the volunteer texted me daily with updates on Noah, my attitude and heart softened toward organized religion, Christianity in particular. This is not to say that other religions are not charitable or do not try to help the homeless. But I think Christian churches have the market cornered on helping the homeless, certainly in downtown L.A.

John had my cell phone number because we had to attach a number to Noah's registration there. John would text me daily to say Noah looked good or he was watching him outside. He told me to have faith in the Lord and to not give up on my son. I was touched by the kindness of this stranger. He had confided in me that he was once a drug addict, but the Lord saved him.

When John asked for money from me months later, I had a feeling that he must have fallen off the wagon. I didn't ask him why he was no longer living at the Union Rescue Mission. He said he just needed money for groceries to get him through the end of the month. I went to Western Union for the first time and wired him the money. Four years later, I heard my cell phone receiving texts in the middle of the night. I waited until morning to check my phone. John, the born again Christian and a former volunteer at Union Rescue Mission had sent me a dick pic and a short message about how attracted he was to me and how he still intends to pay me back the money I sent him. I didn't respond because it was obvious this was a sick man. I felt sorry for him. No reason to be mad or offended. I just blocked him.

Both the insanity in my son and the panic inside me were ramping up now that he landed on Skid Row. Only the Coroner's office would be worse. Even though Noah had reserved a cot for two solid weeks, he lost his reservation twice by not adhering to the 7:30 p.m. curfew. None of this made sense to me. He could be inside an air-conditioned building with piles of clean donated clothes to pick from, with clean bathrooms available and a security guard at the front door. There was even an interior atrium-like patio where he could go to smoke. Instead, he preferred to sit outside all night. He preferred to chain smoke and watch all the antics and drug-related activity going on in front of the shelter. I don't know whether he was afraid to fall asleep or genuinely entertained by the parade of lunacy and Third World poverty.

I tried three times to get him re-registered for a cot at the shelter. John the volunteer didn't seem annoyed at all. He must have seen this waffling before. Each time, Noah said he preferred to stay outside and this is when I felt I was losing him as a son. He was not "hitting rock bottom" the way an alcoholic might wake up in an alley and finally realize they needed to get sober. 2016 was a very hot summer, probably still 75 degrees out at 2:00 in the morning, so he never experienced the even harsher aspects of homelessness in cold, snow, or daily rain.

His therapist and case manager, who were just weeks away from dropping him as a client, came down to see him a few times in front of the shelter. He told them he was okay and did not need their help. Because of the truly crazy laws in our nation, they could only help someone who voluntarily accepts help, so there was not much they could do.

Decades ago and continuing to this day, we give people who are incapable of making rational good decisions regarding their safety the ability to choose "danger to self and others". We repeat this insanity endangering the lives of citizens and the mentally ill. All in the name of "civil rights," this encourages the likelihood a mentally ill person will end up losing their civil rights anyway when they commit a petty crime or hurt another individual, or worse. All of this pain for the person, their family, and the public could be avoided.

This was the low point in my struggles to provide even the essentials for Noah, and I did not want him to know how dangerous his plight was. I tried to make it less scary and provided him with a backpack to store a few things like bottled water and cigarettes. He didn't want anything else. I gave him a fanny pack so he could put a debit card in it and hide it under his shirt. I didn't want it in view or easily accessible to anyone who might steal it. He never wanted to hold anything, so I figured a backpack could help him, but then I realized he looked like every other homeless person in filthy clothes with a backpack. On the nearest street corner, a predatory man asked each person passing by if they would sell their California ID in exchange for $150. Now we know how non-citizens can get fake ID. Years earlier I made a practice of giving Noah only a laminated copy of his actual ID card which had to be replaced each time he put everything he owned in a dumpster or left behind after each eviction. I kept the original, along with his social security card. I couldn't trust that he wouldn't lose or sell them. It's easy to assume homeless people have no family or friends; they were abandoned. This is no doubt true in many cases. There are also people like myself, parents trying to get help for their loved one, even when they resist help to the point of homelessness.

Every few days he would call to say he had either lost the debit card or gave it to someone who did not return it. He was losing or giving away everything. He went through a few fanny packs and backpacks and I started to feel embarrassed, going to the bank twice a week for four weeks to repeatedly ask them to issue a new debit card. I ended up confessing to the bank teller and he said I could continue to get the debit cards replaced, as long as I did not claim they had fraudulent charges on them. At some point, I speculated Noah was giving the debit cards to people in exchange for drugs, but I didn't bother to ask because I knew I would not get a truthful answer. I could easily assume he owed people money and might have told people to go and try to get money from an ATM machine nearby. I could tell on line some-one was trying to withdraw money that was not available, many times per day. This possibility scared me because of memories from the previous year when a housekeeper at a Board and Care said a guy was hunting Noah down for money owed. This was one of the times Noah had gone missing, unaware that a man in the neighborhood wanted to kill him.

I was never a typical "Jewish mom," but these scenarios brought out the Jewish culture buried deep inside of me. I wasn't supposed to have a son who was wanted by a drug dealer! I wasn't supposed to have a son who was too ill to take care of himself! I wasn't supposed to have a son wandering around Skid Row. I'll never get to be the Jewish mom who says with pride, "My Son, the Doctor!" Not by a long shot. On the one hand, Jews are credited with inventing psychotherapy (Sigmund Freud, Alfred Adler, and "honorary Jew" Carl Jung) and we tend to make fun of our neuroses, especially on TV sit-coms or by elevating it to an art form like Woody Allen. While I have not been a practicing Jew since childhood, the cultural sensibilities are in my DNA.

Compare that to some cultures where mental illness is still taboo and not discussed openly. In other cultures, a mentally ill person may become a total outcast. It wasn't even that long ago when people thought the mentally ill were possessed by the Devil and deserved their misery. Some families remain in denial for the longest time to the detriment of their ill loved ones who could be getting better if the family would pro-actively intervene.

When I speak before law enforcement in their Crisis Intervention Training programs, officers have acknowledged they respond differently in certain neighborhoods as they have learned what to expect. People of Asian descent, for example, may harbor a tremendous amount of shame around mental illness and are the least likely to seek out mental health services. In one such reported case in Los Angeles County in 2015, a Chinese woman named Lai Hang received a cancer diagnosis with only four months to live. Her 18-year-old son, George, suffered from schizophrenia and she was terrified he would become a mass shooter. In a bizarre rationale to save her son from causing harm to strangers or becoming a burden to others after she died, Lai Hang purchased a gun, took George to a nearby motel, and shot him to death. She confessed to the crime to "punish" herself. In jail, her cancer spread quickly and a judge granted her "compassionate release" to die soon after in a hospital.

The "adventures" with Noah on Skid Row in downtown Los Angeles would continue on and off for two months. Sometimes I would get calls in the middle of the night, where a hardly recognizable voice would ask me to put more money on the debit card, so I could "hook him up." One time I went to bring him another debit card and he was sprawled out on the sidewalk in front of the mission, eyes closed. As I approached him, he looked like he could be dead. Maybe he felt it was safer to sleep in broad daylight than at night. Before Noah landed on Skid Row, he had been steadily gaining weight, upwards of 200 pounds on his 5' 6" frame. He quickly lost a noticeable amount of weight while homeless. He was eating less, walking more, probably doing drugs, and I'm sure the stress registered in his body in other ways too. He managed not to get sunburned, but his clothes were stained, he had a grimy tan and dirt under his fingernails.

I sat on the sidewalk with him, leaning up against the shelter's wall, trying to have a conversation and filling him in on what kinds of housing alternatives I had come up with. I always try to act normal and calm with him, even in the face of emergencies. We sat next to another young homeless man who leaned over to me and said Noah had "good diction." I found it ironic and told this young black man he had "good diction" to know what the word "diction" means. As we sat on the ground, on an otherwise sunny summer day, a group of twenty plus social workers and government officials passed us by. They had clipboards in hand and laminated ID's hanging around their necks. It was obvious they were touring the homeless encampments, trying not to look directly in the eyes of any of the thousands in desperate need.

One day, I naively called the police department closest to Skid Row. I asked them if they would go to where Noah was camped out and do a 5150 if I told them my son needed hospitalization. Sounding like a "cop character" straight out of central casting, the officer on duty said, "Lady, there are 11,000 homeless people down here. We can't do anything unless we see a crime in progress or if there has been obvious *foul* play." With the parade of government officials passing by Noah and me on the pavement, even I felt like a zoo animal on display. A year later, I would recognize that spot where we sat when it was flashed on the evening news; it was the same spot where police shot to death a homeless man nicknamed "Africa". Only weeks after we got Noah off Skid Row, there was an incident where many homeless were hospitalized for taking a "bad batch" of synthetic marijuana called "Spice." That emergency round up probably would have included my son, as he told me several times that he wanted to get "Spice" because it was legal.

After a couple of weeks, the therapist and case manager secured a place for Noah. It was not a typical licensed Board and Care. It was called a Collaboration House. I would only learn later that this was not an appropriate place for him, but beggars can't be choosers. The Collaboration Houses are for the formerly home-less, and generally higher functioning people. The residents may have mental illness as well, but these homes are set up for people who are stable and compliant with their medications. They are single-family dwellings, usually three or four-bedroom houses with two people in each bedroom.

These houses are donated for use, by homeowners who know that the houses will suffer a lot of wear and tear and have more occupants than what most landlords prefer. No background checks needed. But some owners offer their homes out of the goodness of their hearts and they receive just about the market value of their lease potential, partially compensated by the Department of Mental Health. The extra financial burden, however, is that the homeowner must provide for all furnishings, TV, and a land-line phone for the house. The owner also has additional obligations like having more than one refrigerator and supplying bedding, kitchenware, and basic toiletries.

The Collaboration House policies require people to shop, make their food, and clean up after themselves. They need to volunteer for household chores and attend regular Twelve Step meetings. In

2016, the average rent at a Collaboration House was $500.00 per month. These basic requirements were beyond my son at that time. The therapist thought Noah would like living in a single-family home better than a larger noisy Board and Care. She thought it was worth a try and the Collaboration House facilitator wanted to give him a chance.

As an aside, the process of getting Noah to qualify for this program was almost sabotaged by the fact he was not listed in a county "homeless database." This struck me as cruelly absurd since so many homeless and mentally ill people have fallen through the cracks. How does the county expect them to get on a homeless database or even know one exists? It reminded me of another housing agency where they provide residences for people who must be homeless at the time they call with an apartment opening. I asked someone who worked there how a homeless person could even find out when their place on the waiting list was up. She said I would be surprised how many homeless people have cell phones or case managers!

The larger question was whether or not a person freshly off the street was even able to manage in their apartment, without also having substantial mental health and disability services as a requirement to their placement. Other programs across the country have shown that just providing a person with mental illness a place to live is not enough. It could even prove to be a danger to themselves and others. One program in New York followed up on the people placed in their apartments, only to find some living in squalor, not taking medications, and in full-blown psychotic relapse. The people put in their apartments proved they were better off living in the loosely monitored Board and Cares. Some people even expressed a desire to return to the sub-par Board and Care they came from, instead of living by themselves, isolated. As I write this, the Corona Virus Pandemic of 2020 is in full swing and many homeless people are being placed in hotels, shut down for regular business. The result should be interesting.

This Collaboration House was surprisingly nice. The clean kitchen had granite counters and there was an upstairs den with a skylight. Within days in this fresh setting, the house manager alerted me that Noah was eating other residents' food and not cleaning up after himself: Déjà vu for the umpteenth time. I phoned an agency called IHSS, an acronym for In-Home Support Services. It can take a while to get approved for this program, but they offer hired help who grocery shop, cook, and clean. I tried to make sure he could stay at the Collaboration House and not return to the streets. A few more days passed and they told me he could not live there anymore before we even had a chance to hire IHSS support. Noah acted agitated and other residents reported his inappropriate behaviors. They understandably require stability and no one else living there should feel threatened by the actions of another resident.

I could not bring Noah home with me. I could not trust he would act appropriately or safely in my own home either. I still had the ultimate goal to get him into a higher level of care and this would not happen if I were to bring him home. That's why many parents allow for some pretty precarious situations to continue: If we bring our adult child home and there is an incident that requires calling the police or a mental health evaluation team, our loved one will often be declined help. Aside from any immediate emergency, the police or psych evaluation team will see the person has a roof over their head and presumably food to eat. Because of the obscene lack of resources available for mentally ill people, the priorities have to go to those out on the street, causing problems to the public at large, like running around in traffic. Those folks get priority emergency treatment, after the fact, when they did something criminal or blatantly dangerous.

The statistics are always in flux, usually trending upwards. As of 2010, 3.4% of Americans were suffering from mental illness, over eight million, with only fourteen psychiatric beds available per 100,000 people. There used to be 380 beds per 100,000 throughout the United States; "de-institutionalization," a word with negative connotations, is to blame. Bringing our mentally ill relative home to live with us, even temporarily, can sabotage a larger plan to get our loved one hospitalized. What a choice a parent has to make! We have to risk something truly awful and life-threatening happening to our sick child until they get some help. I once called the Department of Mental Health regarding housing and with no compassionate resources to offer they said, "Sometimes it has to get worse before it gets better." For all the talk and anti-stigma campaigns regarding "preventing" mental illness in children, there is a major blind spot when it comes to preventing full-blown tragedies for those who have *already* been identified as ill and need treatment. Sadly, the neediest are the last priority.

When the Collaboration House asked me to pick my son up, I begged them to call a PET team to evaluate him and see if he could get hospitalized. He had been off his medication a full month. They agreed to try and they kept him on the premises until the PET team arrived. This proved to be a creative challenge for the house director, as they had never assisted with a potential 5150 before, further evidence that Collaboration houses are not appropriate places for lower functioning people with SMI (serious mental illness). They offered Noah food and conversation; otherwise, he would have walked away from the house to panhandle and God-Knows-What.

Fortunately, the psych team called me before they left the Collaboration House. The woman in charge told me my son seemed fine and did not fit the criteria for a 5150 psychiatric hold. Sound familiar? At that point, I gave her an earful and pleaded with her to do the hold. I emailed her cell phone a couple of prepared documents going over Noah's mental health history and his recent homelessness.

Once she had a better understanding of what was going on, she agreed to call an ambulance. I breathed a sigh of relief because I thought he would get hospitalized. I figured I just had to wait until I heard from him. Sometimes I have been able to find out what hospital he's been admitted to right away and sometimes I have to wait for Noah to call me himself from the hospital payphone. No matter how psychotic my son was, he was fairly responsible for letting me know where he is, eventually. This is not the case with other parents I know. Their very ill son or daughter will refuse to let them know where they are or give hospital staff permission to call.

A day later, Noah called me from an Urgent Care clinic. He said he was ready to be picked up and I was stunned. Why had he not been taken to the hospital? Well, there could have been several reasons that I will never know, but the Urgent Care clinic was across the street from a major hospital, a place where he had been in the ER for five days, just a little over a year before. I can only assume they had no bed for him and just turned him over to the nearby Urgent Care Clinic. I pleaded with the Urgent Care nurse to keep him there until a hospital bed could be obtained, but they had no intention of accommodating me. The nurse threatened that if I didn't pick Noah up immediately she would report me to Adult Protective Services! I reminded her I had no legal responsibility to pick him up. I learned early on a parent should refuse to pick up their son or daughter, in order for the clinic or hospital to work harder at finding an appropriate place-ment. Once again, they threatened to give him a bus token and directions to the nearest shelter. Aside from all the local patient dumping going on, mental health agencies from other states put people on a one-way bus ride to Los Angeles, the Mecca of U.S. homelessness, just to get them out of other cities.

I called the supervisor of the clinic and told him the nurse threatened to report me to various agencies. I told her I was my son's Representative Payee for SSI benefits, but that didn't obligate me to be responsible for his housing or treatment.

The clinic supervisor did not say much. He sounded calm and told me he would "handle the situation." I assumed he was going to tell the nurse to cool her jets and to be more respectful on the phone. I also assumed they would make an effort to get him hospitalized. Even the treating psychiatrist at that clinic agreed that he should be hospitalized, once she learned about his recent health history and homelessness.

Several days passed. I was concerned, but I also thought it was highly likely that Noah had been admitted to some hospital and the staff had not gotten around to getting a verbal consent from him to contact me. Oh, how wrong I was!

On Day Four, I got a phone call from a woman who said that she was calling because Noah had given her my number. She said she knew he didn't belong in the neighborhood and was concerned after seeing him walking around. She let Noah speak to me on her cell phone for a few minutes. I found out that he was not in a very safe area. I was walking out the door to an appointment I could not cancel when his call came in and I had to tell Noah I could not pick him up immediately. It would be a couple of hours. There was a 7/Eleven store across the street from where he was standing, so I told him to stay in that area and expect me there in two hours. He had been walking around for four days, so what're another two hours?

On my way there, I picked up another debit card for him. I was furious he had not been hospitalized. I found out later the Urgent Care clinic discharged him with a prescription to fill across the street and sent him on his way. In the days that had passed, I was trying to secure emergency housing or shelter for Noah but had not been successful. It's horrendous how many dead end leads one has to sift through, trying to get help.

When I reached Noah, he seemed calm, but spaced out. He even laughed a little to himself, singing some lyrics from the Led Zeppelin song, *Dazed and Confused*. No kidding, I thought a tiny morsel of the "old" Noah saw the absurdity of this situation. He still had the last backpack I had given him and the inside held nothing except three medication bottles. I pulled them out, only to find all nearly empty. It dawned on me he might have taken nearly a month's worth of three different anti-psychotics in a matter of days. It didn't quite register it was a 'non-fatal' overdose. What I should have done in retrospect was call 911. I should have had an ambulance come and pick him up right there in the parking lot. I should have told the medics that he had over-dosed and they would have rushed him to an emergency room. From there, I might have been able to convince the hospital he was a "danger to self and others" and he should be admitted for psychiatric care. I didn't think of that until much later. Instead, I drove Noah right back to the Union Rescue Mission where he had been weeks before.

I made him promise to go inside and sign up for a cot. I told him it would only be temporary and I was on the verge of securing a bed for him at another shelter ten minutes from my house, which was true. While Noah had been walking around aimlessly in a bad neighborhood, I had found a Transitional house, which called itself a shelter. It was a single-family home in a decent neighborhood, with beds paid for by the Department of Mental Health. They had social workers come daily to counsel the residents and help them get into long-term housing. Young men would stay there anywhere from a couple of weeks to a couple of months.

This wholesome clean "Transitional" house did not have any openings but told me to call daily to find a vacancy. They only had eight beds, but men were coming and going quickly. I couldn't bring Noah home with me. I knew he would not get the help he needed if he was coming from mom's house and that is the sorry truth when it comes to the broken mental health care system.

Noah did not register for a cot, as I had begged him to. I tracked some of his moves on-line based on the purchases he made with the debit card. He was in the area, buying things at the markets on each end of the block where I dropped him off. Even though he may have over-dosed, he was ambulatory and eating. We were back to Square One. I still don't know if Noah understood the dire straits he was in. On the one hand, he told me a year later he had chronic pain in the middle of his back from where someone kicked him when he was "down on San Pedro." He couldn't quite say the words "when I was homeless." On the other hand, Skid Row is just a few city blocks away from an upscale area and Japan Town, where he took himself at least once that summer, to panhandle and buy himself sushi. He also walked around the discount clothing district. I guess he had some experiences that were fun for him, despite everything else wrong with this picture.

Back on Skid Row and after Noah had been evicted from the Collaboration House, he had not been successfully placed in a hospital, and his treatment team was even closer to dropping him as a client, at a time when he needed them the most. Paid for by the state of California through the Mental Health Services Act, the Full-Service Partnership programs are voluntary services. They cannot force someone to work with them. However, their motto, "whatever it takes" felt like bull crap to me.

I didn't think they were trying hard enough to keep him as a client. I couldn't tell them how to do their job, but he might have agreed to continue meeting with them with just a little more prodding, or a Happy Meal. (The treatment team knew very well they were disengaging with a person who had no insight into his illness or the dangers before him). One of the ways mental health care agencies can secure continued funding year after year is through statistics showing how successful they are in treating people. If you only treat people who are compliant and don't include the non-compliant in the statistics, the success rate appears better than it is.

The next day, Noah borrowed someone's phone to tell me his glasses had fallen off and someone walked by and smashed them. This was the last straw. Not only was my son homeless and filthy, but he was also now nearly blind! I had a very old pair of spare glasses for him that was not his current prescription. It would take a week or more to get him another good pair of glasses. I called Noah's father in desperation and told him I couldn't take it anymore. Most of the time I tried to handle every problem by myself, and Noah's father didn't intervene. Sometimes I had to reach out to him, whenever I reached a breaking point. I couldn't stand that Noah was homeless and not able to see! What if he crossed the street and got hit by a car? Just weeks prior, Noah told me he witnessed someone on Skid Row cross the street and get hit by a truck. Noah was traumatized and told me the poor guy's body was dismembered by the impact of the accident! Noah was disturbed that none of the police officers asked him if he was okay from what he had just witnessed. All I could say is the police offi- cers needed to secure the crime scene as their priority. Because it crossed my mind Noah might have been lying or hallucinating, I made a call to someone very familiar with Skid Row. This person confirmed cars hit homeless people, regularly.

Noah's father agreed to split the costs of putting him in a motel. I picked him up and brought him to my area and booked him in another motel. I was still calling the Transitional house daily for vacancy updates. Noah could barely be trusted to stay in a motel by himself and not do inappropriate things, but I had to get him off of Skid Row and indoors with a bed. Nearby stores within walking distance sold him food. I checked on him daily, but the motel manager was not pleased. At the end of the week, they declined to let us book more days. The housekeeper reported to the motel manager that Noah had stunk up the room pretty bad and made a big mess. Noah was doing pretty much nothing except shredding up large amounts of paper in the room and probably smoking in there too, which was not allowed.

We went across the street to book him in another motel and this one also had a hard time not evicting him. One night I got a call at 11 p.m. and the manager said Noah was panhandling to other guests of the motel and sitting on the ground in the middle of the parking lot smoking. He was making a mess of his room and they thought he was either taking drugs or dealing drugs.

During the motel chapter of this saga, I spoke on the phone with the medical director of the Department of Mental Health. He had a reputation for being a real Godsend in removing some of the most frustrating obstacles parents go through.

I emailed him initially because a friend insisted I tell him how the Urgent Care Clinic discharged Noah when he should have been hospitalized.

The Department of Mental Health (DMH) contracts with that particular Urgent Care clinic and DMH needed to know how badly they treated a patient. The Urgent Care Clinic released a gravely ill person to the streets, expecting him to take his medication appropriately while unsupervised and homeless. My friend told me that if I didn't report the Urgent Care Clinic to DMH she would. I emailed the Medical Director at 5 p.m. on a Friday. He called me back on the phone late the next day, a Saturday afternoon, and I was stunned. I had not even expected any reply, let alone a reply within twenty-four hours and by phone. He was interested in talking to me at length about Noah's case.

In my email letter, I complained about how the Urgent Care clinic treated him and how they were responsible for him over-dosing, where he could have died. As an afterthought, I wrote at the end of the email that I would like to also speak with him about my less-than-stellar experiences with the FSP program who dumped Noah when he needed them the most, and the AOT program, who told me he was on at least a two-month waiting list. AOT (Assisted Outpatient Treatment) is a voluntary program that picks up where the FSP program leaves off. AOT is a support program only recently funded and implemented by our County; they worked longer with individuals, who were in worse shape than those in the FSP program.

At the time my son needed their services, they turned me away because they had an instant waiting list. I wanted this for Noah because they engaged with the ill person longer to gain their trust and have them agree to treatment.

If a person needs FSP (Full Service Partnership), a therapist comes to visit a person and asks them if they would like help in any way. If the person says no, the FSP team will not return. With Assisted Outpatient Treatment (AOT), the person had to have a documented history of non-compliance in many ways. If they refuse treatment initially, the AOT team still visits them for a month or two, before they decide to quit. AOT services are now available in other states besides California. AOT staff will even visit homeless people if they can reliably find them. They might talk to the ill person on the street, get them some food or clothing, and let the person know they are available to help. On an individual basis, if the ill person still refuses treatment, AOT agencies can obtain a court order from Mental Health Court for treatment. Some who are court-ordered into treatment will start to cooperate with the AOT team.

When the FSP team dropped my son as a client (absurd timing), at least the therapist put in a request that AOT take over. At first, AOT refused to accept the application because they said he was already being treated by FSP. This is the kind of illogical, crazy-making response I encountered regularly. I had to call AOT and state the obvious: the application for AOT was precisely *because* FSP was dropping him as a client. In reality, he was not going to be under their care much longer at *their* request. I re-submitted the application and was then told it would be a two-month wait before anyone would come out to see Noah.

Now, imagine what it would be like if someone called a Suicide Hotline, was put on hold for thirty minutes, and then told they were being referred to someone else with a two-month wait before someone could speak with them! I told the Medical Director all of this and that my son should have been seamlessly transferred from the FSP program to the AOT program. Dr. Stein took it all in and said on the following Tuesday he would go to the AOT offices and speak with them.

Dr. Stein also said that based on Noah's history, he should be in an IMD, (Institute for Mental Disease) or "sub-acute care." Dr. Stein was also aware I was trying to get Noah into the Transitional shelter near my home in the meantime.

Just in time, as Noah was being asked to leave the second motel, there was an opening at the Transitional shelter and I moved him over there. Then, days later, the AOT office called me to say they were ready to initiate outreach to Noah.

AOT called to say they were ready to meet Noah on the same day Dr. Stein went to their weekly meeting. He demanded they put Noah at the head of the line. I was grateful for getting "special treatment," but sickened the system as a whole does not work expediently for all. To recap, it's the summer of 2016. It's been *ten* years since Noah's schizophrenia raised its ugly head.

In what appeared as a random chain of events, I finally made a personal connection with Dr. Stein, top of the food chain in the labyrinth of the L.A. County Department of Mental Health. By now, I haven't cried in years. I'm all cried out.

The AOT team started visiting Noah and told him they were working on finding him a place to live. The young social worker assigned to Noah was already buying him snacks, a radio, and trying to get him to warm up to her. But it was a horrible week at the Transitional shelter. Noah refused to go to their household meetings. He caused property damage and went AWOL twice. After the first time, they warned him not to do it again, but Noah was unhinged.

A rational person would have been grateful, just to have a clean room to sleep in, access to a bathroom and meals served to him. But he was off his medication and he was probably *on* some kind of street drug. I later learned people can get single doses of crystal meth for as little as five or ten dollars. Noah was an expert in panhandling, so he could maintain a drug habit on the streets. Over the years I have been very naïve about a lot of things. The second time he went missing, it was preceded by a voicemail message he left me, which still haunts me. It was one of the lowest points in our relationship as mother and son. Before this threatening phone call, the program director at the Transitional shelter told me to stop coming by each morning to give Noah money. I was not intentionally trying to be an enabler. I was trying to exact some restraint in his behaviors, by bringing him just enough cash each day to buy a finite number of cigarettes and a soda.

I learned from the past that Noah could not save or budget and that even giving him money to last for a few days was not going to be managed properly.

The program director wanted me to stop giving Noah any money at all until he participated in the shelter's meetings. I was in a whole-hearted agreement.

Not more than a day went by without me bringing him money and Noah went berserk. He kicked in the front door at the Transitional shelter, he submerged their house cell phone in the kitchen sink water and he left me a voicemail message, calling me various profanities.

He then went on to say he was going to "curb stomp" me and crush my skull in a million pieces. All this from a son who had previously never said such insulting things to me, all this from a son who once called himself my "Mini-me". As a small boy, he made a Mother's Day card that read, "Don't ever die I love you so much." Now, 25 years old, suffering from schizophrenia and fueled with crystal meth, he wants to "crush my skull" because I didn't bring him ten dollars. I didn't even know what "curb stomp" meant and I had to look it up on the internet. I was disgusted and a little afraid. Was it the psychosis talking or street drugs? I called the police station in the neighborhood where the Transitional shelter was located. The officer who answered said that he couldn't do anything about a threatening statement because I was not in that service area and I was not at imminent risk.

I then called the police station nearest my home and they also told me they could not do anything unless Noah arrived at my property. They asked if he had access to a car, but Noah does not even drive, so they viewed my situation as even less of a priority. On this day, August 20, 2016, I truly wondered if I had lost my son completely and I would have to disown him. The day seemed additionally ominous because it was August 20, 1990, that I know I conceived Noah, twenty-six years ago to the day. We were trying to get pregnant and I took a pregnancy test that day. On August 20, 2000, my ex-husband threatened to sue me over a custody dispute. I hate August 20th.

Some parents still maintain contact with their ill son or daughter, even when threats were made and even when there was violence.

Some parents still advocate on behalf of their sick loved one, even when they have a restraining order against them. I couldn't go to that level, however. Somewhere along the line, I heard there is an average of one matricide per month in the County where I lived.

Noah went AWOL from the Transitional shelter again after six days and even after the AOT social worker had established a nice rapport with him. She tried to inspire Noah by promising that AOT would be finding him more permanent housing fairly soon. Unlike Skid Row, where Noah stayed within a certain square block range, now I didn't know where he was. Without a debit card, he had to resort to panhandling to survive. This third stint at homelessness pushed me to the point where I had asked my internist for anti-anxiety medication for myself. This was a big step because I had to admit to myself and someone else the level of stress had gotten so bad I couldn't handle it any longer. I needed medical intervention myself. I only took the Ativan a couple of times because it hardly made a difference and I didn't want to become reliant on them.

Six days and nights passed without a word from Noah. Then one night I got a call from a police officer. Someone had called 911 and the police officer went to check on Noah, who had been in a neighborhood not more than five miles from my house. The officer never told me why someone called 911. Perhaps Noah looked lost or disoriented. Perhaps he was panhandling. Noah did tell him to call me and I urged the officer to do the 5150 to get him hospitalized. The officer told me he appeared fine and didn't fit the criteria for a hold. I again launched into the backstory about how he was homeless, going AWOL from a shelter, and that the Department of Mental Health was trying to work with him. I told the officer Noah was off his meds, but the officer was reluctant to do anything. Then the officer said he would call me back in a few minutes. He tried to get a PET team to come and do a psychiatric evaluation on Noah, but the officer said he already got word there were no hospital beds available. The Mobile Psych team was not coming out. The officer's parting words to me were, "It's not a crime to be homeless" and he went on his way.

TWELVE:

Just What the Doctor Ordered

The next morning Noah was sitting on my driveway. I called 911 and told the operator my son was psychotic and needed to be 5150'd. I told her that only a week before he had verbally threatened me. The operator said the police were on their way. While waiting for the police to arrive, I stayed on the phone with her.

I had no idea if the police car was patched into the conversation, to hear the back-story on what they would be addressing when they got to my house. I kept giving the operator more information and details, in hopes that it would ensure the police acted appropriately when they arrived.

Almost all of us know by now that many altercations between mentally ill people and law enforcement do not go well. I understand police have one of the most stressful jobs on the planet and they have to make split-second decisions, sometimes proving fatal. Sometimes it is their fault and sometimes not. Many mentally ill people provoke "suicide by cop." I later learned the 911 operator calls the police and gives them only a minimal amount of information about the nature of the emergency. This is so unfortunate because police do not have details before they go into a potentially dangerous situation; they walk in blind. We have satellites in space that can zoom in on a penny in the street, but we don't have a way for police to listen to the 911 call while driving to the scene!

The police arrived quickly and Noah was sitting "Indian style" on my driveway when I went outside. Two male officers and a female officer surrounded him and went through the protocols to pat him down and make sure he was not armed. I stood about ten feet away from Noah, almost having an out-of-body experience, while they asked him certain questions. Noah was cooperative and courteous and there was only one give-away he wasn't thinking clearly. One officer asked him how long it had been since he had eaten and Noah said, "It's been years."

I had been a volunteer speaker at the CIT (Crisis Intervention Training) seminars for law enforcement for about a year. I go as a family member to tell the police and sheriffs in attendance what it is like to be the mother of a son with schizophrenia. Putting a human face on this tragedy and giving them tips on how to better handle the mentally ill is all part of their training. I now had another true story to tell, for the next time I would speak at CIT training. I could tell them how expertly my neighborhood police department handled my son. The female officer was quite attractive. Think- Heather Locklear as Officer Stacey Sheridan in the 1980's TV Show *T.J. Hooker*. My son ended up trotting off with her to the squad car and I know he noticed how pretty she was. You couldn't *not* notice.

In the CIT training, the officers learn many ways to effectively dialogue with an agitated person and they even get a few tips from the guest speakers, like me. Offering a distressed individual some food, a cigarette, or even a kind smile can go a long way. One very important tip the officers learn is to speak directly to the person under duress and not just the other people around them, as if the ill person doesn't exist. This show of respect and compassion can go a long way in having effective communication and a non-violent outcome. Seeing the female officer reminded me of the time I co-presented at a CIT training with a woman who had survived an incredibly dramatic life due to her mental illness. She was in much better shape when we met and able to tell her story before a room full of men, knowing some of them didn't want to be there. Even though she had had many encounters with the law as a drug addict and prostitute in her past, the energy in the room palpably changed when she divulged she had family members in law enforcement. In one pivotal incident, a psychotic break left her completely naked in a park when the police found her. A female officer put her at ease, covered her in a blanket, got her some clothing, and managed to get her to a shelter for women. In certain situations, I think female officers should be the first choice to answer the call.

Noah cooperated fully and my boyfriend Ron wanted to make sure the police would do something, not like the officer the night before. Ron came out of the house with his cell phone, ready to play the copy he made of the voicemail message Noah left me a week prior, threatening to "curb stomp" me. Ron wanted the officers to hear Noah threatening me, as a way to seal the deal and make sure the 5150 happened. As soon as he tried to play the recording, Officer #1 told him to stop! He said it with the same tone as when the police say, "Put your hands up!" Ron was bewildered by this response, but he followed orders. Only after the female officer took Noah away to the squad car did Officer #1 explain his response. Since Noah was cooperating, he didn't want anything to agitate Noah, such as hearing a recording of his voice swearing at his mother. The officer further explained he didn't want to get hurt, nor did he want to hurt Noah. Even though the recording was the compelling evidence Noah needed to be put on a hold, the police didn't want to listen to it.

Both male officers remained in our driveway for about ten minutes after Noah left with the female officer. They were proud to tell us they had received Mental Health Awareness training and a well-known psychiatrist affiliated with the Department of Mental Health sometimes rides along with them to mental health emergencies. I will always be grateful to those officers, who did not hesitate to get Noah hospitalized. It turned out to be a pivotal hospitalization, the one I was waiting for all summer. An unexpected nice touch arrived a few days later when one of the officers called and asked me how I was and what mental health resources I might need for my son. I almost fell on the floor!

As soon as all the police left, I called the hospital's emergency room and got their fax number. I faxed over several pages of Noah's Mental Health History and current symptoms. These are the one-pagers I had already prepared; I learned how to make them from a local woman who teaches seminars on getting your loved one conserved. The one-pagers are designed to give any mental health professional a bullet-point snapshot of the mentally ill person's level of functionality and psychosis. With the absence of this information, all too many sick people are not even admitted to psychiatric care or are discharged too early. Even people out of touch with reality often fool mental health professionals into thinking they are stable enough to not need emergency care. Unlike his previous 5150, where he stayed in the emergency room lobby for five days, Noah was admitted fairly quickly.

I sent the same fax to the psychiatric wing because I could not trust the information sent to the Emergency Room would be attached to his file and seen by the staff taking over in another department. It wasn't carried over to the psychiatric wing and this is another reason why parents are coached to deliver these documents, on bright colored paper, in person if they can. Within another 24 hours, I got coaching in how to write a short, two-paragraph plea to the treating hospital psychiatrist that Noah needed to be con-served. Copies were sent to the hospital's Chief of Staff and also the Medical Director of the Department of Mental Health. I wanted the hospital to know their actions and decisions would be monitored and they were accountable to more than just Noah's mother.

One must work quickly to get a hospital to set up a hearing for possible conservatorship. It has to be discussed within three days of admittance and the hospital knows they will likely have the patient stay an extended period. The long hospital stay is not just to get the conservatorship approved, but also to get an appropriate discharge placement. It can take thirty days to get an in-hospital hearing and once the conservatorship has been approved, then God only knows when there will be a bed available at an IMD (Institute of Mental Disease). Not everyone who gets conserved goes to an IMD (which is a locked facility). But the only way to get into a locked facility is through a hospital referral. The exception is you can spend a lot of money on a private attorney to get your loved one conserved. However, this would not guarantee they get admitted to an IMD, especially with their long waiting list.

By definition, when a person is conserved, it means that another adult becomes their legal guardian. This frequently indicates the person needs a higher level of care (at least temporarily) than what is available in the community among outpatient services. The conserved person may very well need to be in a safe, locked environment for a matter of months or a few years. I opted to let the Public Guardian be the conservator because I needed a break from all the drama and I had to assume they would do a good job since they are so experienced. Yet, I also knew the Public Guardian is overloaded with too many cases and prefers it when a family member is a conservator. Part of me agreed to let the Public Guardian be his conservator because I wanted to show Ron I could relinquish control. The intent was to let my son know his behaviors forced me to step back and let the system take over.

While Noah was in the hospital, I visited him a couple of times a week and his attitude and demeanor slowly improved. He was still rather cagey in the beginning and the staff did not seem all that attentive. As far as psych wards go, there is a great variance in the level of care and professionalism or lack of it. At least where Noah was admitted, most of the nurses there looked tired and guarded. There was a depressing blandness and sterile feel to everything around. Doctors were too busy to return phone calls, so a parent must find out when the doctor would be making the rounds at the psychiatric unit. We then try to see if we can interrupt him or her in between patients and steal a few minutes of their time to talk. They don't have time for long discussions and probably feel like they had heard and seen it all.

Noah misrepresented himself with the hospital staff on many occasions and they were oblivious until I corrected their misinformation. One male nurse struck up a conversation with me while I was leaving after a short visit. Noah had told the male nurse that smoking pot was the extent of his drug history. I filled the nurse in on Noah's extensive use of alcohol and many types of drugs: psychedelics, cocaine, crystal meth, etc. The nurse looked confused and embarrassed he had believed the sanitized version he got from my son.

The only thing that may have distinguished Noah from other patients in the hospital at that time was that he got permission to play guitar while there. His father brought what must have been guitar #13 to the hospital. Noah had an OCD pattern of selling guitars and his father couldn't stop himself from replacing them. Playing music is one of the few outlets and activities Noah still enjoys since he became ill. But he doesn't enjoy it as much as he did before when he would play for hours at a time and teach himself how to use recording equipment.

Once people heard how well Noah played guitar, they became friendlier with him. Even the guard in the lobby now recognized me as Noah's mom and when he was on duty on the psych ward,

Noah would give him brief guitar lessons. The nurses kept the guitar behind their front desk and when Noah wanted to play it, he could sit in a big supervised room. Otherwise, a guitar could be used as a "weapon" to hurt someone and the strings on the guitar could be used as a method of suicide, the same reason shoelaces are not allowed in a psych ward. But of course, if someone is determined to end their life, they make it happen right inside a hospital. I heard about one man who hanged himself with his bed sheets strapped to the bathroom door. I heard of another young man who killed himself in the hospital by eating a large amount of toilet paper in the bathroom, choking himself to death near an unaware staff.

The night before Noah was to be discharged, I happened to run into the treating doctor in the elevator. Without looking at me and with one foot out of the elevator, he told me Noah would be discharged to an open Board and Care, (even though he had assured me for five months that Noah would be going to a locked facility). My jaw dropped; I was speechless as he exited the elevator without another word. Since I was not the Conservator, I had no legal say in the matter. I called the Public Guardian the next day to say a terrible mistake was made and Noah should be going to an IMD and not an open "Step Down" Board and Care.

I learned quickly that Public Guardian conservators usually agree with whatever treatment plan doctors and social workers devise, whereas, a parent may have a much better understanding of what their loved one needs. If they are the conservator, they can fight for the more appropriate accommodations, if they are available. A conservator has a list of rights, powers, and duties when they are the legal guardian of an adult with mental illness. The conservatorship has to be renewed every twelve months and with each yearly renewal, the conserved person gets an opportunity to refute their need to be conserved. They get assigned a public defender who informs them of all their rights. This can make for some pretty lively court hearings, much to the dismay and heartache of family members who know better than a judge if their loved one should have their conservatorship terminated.

My son did not have a real understanding of the meaning or scope of a conservatorship. He was under the impression he needed to be conserved to find housing and other services. When it came time for the first year's renewal, he didn't know he could object to being conserved. He thought the hearing was about whether or not to keep the current conservator or get a new one. Once when a judge asked him if he had anything to say, Noah told me he "pleaded the Fifth Amendment." I guess he thought this was the proper way to convey he had nothing to add.

After the five-month-long hospital stay, Noah was placed in an open Board and Care that was supposed to offer more support, with on-site case management and therapy. He did not attend any of those therapy meetings because they are voluntary! Instead, he went right back to panhandling, chain-smoking, doing drugs, and being uncooperative with staff. Five months in a hospital went down the drain. I told the staff at the Board and Care the first day that Noah should have been placed in an IMD and I did not approve of the decision to place him at that Board and Care. I told the AOT team to be on notice that this was a mistake in placement. Sure enough, within two weeks things got so bad they had to call for a psych evaluation and another 5150 hold was ordered. Noah had caused property damage in his bedroom. When I went to pick up his clothes, I saw burned pieces of paper on the floor. My mind raced with fear. I realized if his behaviors had not been halted when they were, he could have added arson on his resume; that would have ruined his life on a whole other level.

They sent Noah to another hospital, but in less than twenty-four hours, he was placed in what they call a temporary IMD.

I knew I would not get a response, but I still felt compelled to let the doctor at the previous hospital know what a mistake it was for them to release Noah to an open facility. By the way, "open facility" means the doors are not locked and residents can come and go as they please.

Often, mental health providers have no accountability whatsoever for the poor decisions they make. I had to get it off my chest and let the hospital treating doctor know that he blew it, big time. Predictably, there was no apology or even acknowledgment from the doctor about my email. Once a doctor releases a patient, they are legally not obligated to communicate any further.

Noah stayed eight months at the temporary IMD. This place offered a little bit more in the way of activities than the hospital and they even had an outside patio area, where patients could get some sunlight. To be clear; when a person is put on a 72-hour hold or even voluntarily admitted to a hospital, I am referring to the type of community hospital where people go for any medical matters. Not all hospitals have psychiatric units, however. A parent can consider him or herself lucky if the hospital closest to where they live has a psychiatric unit. Otherwise, the SMI person will be taken further away and wherever they have an opening. It can also get pricey if the ambulance service is not contracted with the hospital they are going to.

The IMD is also a hospital, specifically a psychiatric hospital, which is kept locked. Patients cannot leave unless they have been there for a while and have proven to be stable enough to not be a flight risk. Escorted by a family member, they can go out for lunch or a brief outing. Having to go through two locked gates to visit Noah, it still felt like a prison or an animal habitat at the zoo. I can't state enough the kinds of environments for mentally ill people are the environments that would make a "normal" person despondent and maybe even, over time, experience a mental breakdown because of it. One time a hospital staff member told me they don't always turn on the air conditioner because they don't want patients to get too comfortable there!

After nearly eight months, the discharge planners had a recommendation for a longer-term IMD. Their choice didn't sit well with me. I looked at the facility up on-line and there were some bad reviews of the place. They had been fined by the state for some unprofessional conduct on the part of the staff. Who knows how many infractions an IMD can rack up before they are closed or some other legal penalties are levied. In one report, a resident who was very sick was not given proper medical care and he died as a result. How unsettling to know that a mentally ill loved one could be neglected or abused, even in a locked facility, and especially by staff members! In one case I know of personally, a mother asked if she could take her son out of the IMD for emergency medical care and was told that if she took him out, he could not be re-admitted. This is one way an IMD can get rid of a difficult patient.

The location of this troubling IMD was in one of the highest crime rate areas in the County. Would I even feel safe visiting him and parking my car on the street? I asked if we could skip that IMD and wait for an opening at another one. I made my case to the Public Guardian Conservator and they did allow us to pass on that one.

The next IMD had an opening a few weeks later. I was also not thrilled with the facility; I had gone there a few months before to check it out. It felt like a cold, sterile place with few activities for the patients. Like many, it had dirty white walls and floors with dull overhead florescent lights. We missed the opportunity to place Noah at another IMD where they at least had a work-out room and a psychologist who made the rounds with a therapy dog.

What I hoped for was an opening at the one and only IMD close to my own home. But that was too much to ask. All the other IMD's were located anywhere from forty to sixty minutes away. This time I could not refuse to let him go to the opening they had. Even if I had been the conservator, I probably would have been pressured into having him discharged to this IMD, the next opening.

THIRTEEN:

Clozapine

Noah ended up living in the longer term IMD for one year. When he first got there, he did not participate in any of the programs. After a few months, they told him that if he did not start going to the programs, he would not get passes for me to take him out to lunch and he might even lose his smoking privileges. At the IMD, he was allowed to smoke four times per day and that meant more to him than just about anything else. Additionally, Noah knew that if I could take him out to lunch, he would be able to smoke a few extra cigarettes, which he did. I kept my boyfriend Ron abreast of what was happening with Noah, but he hardly responded and didn't ask any questions.

What do these "programs" the IMD's and the Step Down facilities offer? I have asked repeatedly for more specifics, but staff members are usually vague.

Some programs are excuses to get the patients out of their bedrooms and minimize their isolation. This can include a weekly "ice cream social." I guess I should not sit in judgment but the last thing these patients need is an overload of sugar to further aggravate their mood disorders and put on more weight, but no one is asking for my opinion. It's common knowledge for a long time, however, that a good diet and regular exercise can do more to alleviate depression than prescription medications. The IMD may offer art classes or exercise, all voluntary and not well-attended. The facility may also have group discussions about medication management, how to avoid relapse, 12-step programs, money management, personal hygiene coaching, or movie showings. It's to motivate a population that doesn't want to do anything except eat, sleep, and smoke.

Some people with SMI do not always have the attention span to sit in a group discussion or even one-on-one therapy for any length of time. People who are lost in their thoughts and the internal world do not often complain of boredom. And yet, these programs can be very unappealing for the person required to attend. My son doesn't even like to sit in chairs which don't allow him to sit comfortably with his ankles crossed, "Indian style."

Noah used to read above grade level when he was young. Even now, people comment on his large vocabulary, but the schizophrenia so seriously affects his cognitive functioning, he can no longer enjoy reading or even watching TV. He can't follow a storyline. Couple that with his magical thinking: He's told more than one person he can now just hold a book for a few minutes and know what's written inside. One of the few activities he seems to almost enjoy is collecting books he will never read. I make a point of taking him to used book stores so that I don't pay full price for books that he puts on a shelf, gives away, scribbles on or tosses. The schizophrenia has caused severe short-term memory loss. As soon as he hears or reads something, it escapes his memory to the degree that learning new things is an extraordinary challenge. When a person has little or no insight into their illness, these programs also seem like a waste of time or irrelevant.

Certain private programs in the U.S. and abroad have a more holistic approach to recovery and stability for people with SMI. What Noah and many others experienced, through government-sponsored programs, only seemed to warehouse people, pay lip service to their needs, and not provide much in the way of genuine, comprehensive care. Once released from care, a vicious cycle of relapse is more than likely. By this time, I had Noah on a

waiting list to get into a good private program, but I doubted he
would ever agree to live there.

I remember one conversation I had with Noah about a group
he attended where they discussed the harm of street drugs. Noah
assured me he was not going to do street drugs any longer. He
said he was just going to smoke cigarettes. At some point in the
discussion, he said he would not be doing crystal meth anymore,
but not because it was so dangerous. He had some other reason,
like the way it looked or smelled. I'll celebrate any reason he gave
for not doing street drugs, but when I heard his surreal reasoning,
I was not confident it would hold over time.

In the beginning, he was only motivated to attend programs
where he could get something else he wanted, like more cigarettes or vending machine access. His addiction and compulsions
remained untested in a locked facility. I should mention that
although I don't consider these temporary IMD's (Institute for
Mental Disease) to be especially therapeutic in the way they are
currently run, they do serve some needed purposes. For a substance
abuser, it is time for them to "dry out" and get some distance from
their dangerous bad habit.

Because of the lack of IMD beds, hospitals that facilitate obtain-
ing a conservatorship for the patient are then legally obligated to
keep the person in their hospital until an IMD placement opens
up. Since psychiatric hospitalizations are not covered by Medi-Cal
or Medicaid, and since private insurance only pays for a couple of
weeks, the hospitals lose money warehousing patients waiting for
an IMD. This is why the initial hospital is so reluctant to open up
a conservatorship for the many who need them. Behind closed
doors, they probably have a policy about how much their yearly
budget can withstand, holding a certain number of people under
conservatorship, waiting for an IMD bed, knowing they will not
get paid.

The general public also has no idea what a "locked facility" is really like unless they have visited one in person. Decades later, many people still assume a current-day locked facility may be reminiscent of the "Insane Asylums" from centuries past, where people with mental illness were treated worse than criminals in prison. They may also have images from the 1975 Academy award-winning movie *One Flew Over the Cuckoo's Nest,* based on the 1962 novel by Ken Kesey. Back in the 1800s, the asylums allowed visitors to come in and gawk at the patients like carnival freaks. The patients were kept in cages, slept on hay, and were allowed to live in their squalor. We can agree there were many times in the past when the mentally ill were denied their basic civil rights and personal dignity. Nowadays there is not enough intervention because our society has swung to the other extreme.

We are afraid to appear like we are violating someone's civil rights, even at the expense of their sanity. Fortunately, we have come a long way from literally giving people lobotomies without their consent. President John F. Kennedy's sister Rosemary had a lobotomy, which did not go well; none of them did. Before her lobotomy, all the rage at the time, she started to act somewhat promiscuously. After the lobotomy, she could barely function. It is no coincidence the Kennedy political dynasty then took a personal interest in mental health matters, disabilities, and started the Special Olympics. We also have a political climate where higher functioning mentally ill people have been incensed at being held against their will in a hospital or IMD at some point in their lives. They now aggressively try to prevent it from happening to their lower-functioning peers: Well-intended, but also selfish and misguided. Even though I am critical of our current mental health care system, I can say whole-heartedly it is better than nothing!

It never ceases to amaze me how some higher functioning "peers" want to deny lower-functioning peers with the attention and protection they need. Bringing back involuntary treatment on a larger scale is not going to threaten the independence or rights of higher functioning people with mental illness. Many people with serious mental illness are grateful for the intervention and say so, further down the road, when they have more insight into how gravely ill they were. Many recognize they may have died if they had not been treated involuntarily. For the seriously mentally ill neglected too long, they are permanently out of touch with reality and cannot function in an open society. They are not even in the same category as their higher functioning peers who were lucky enough to become stable and politically active. We must acknowledge some people cannot make healthy, safe decisions for themselves and may need an intervention against their will. It's the greater good; the ultimate kindness. Mental health care providers can also release themselves from some of their burdens by just letting family members be more involved!

While Noah was at the IMD, I attended quarterly progress meetings. The Public Guardian conservator never came to a single meeting. At the first progress meeting, one of the staff members assumed I was a nurse, just because I was conversant regarding the medications Noah was on. It's sad to say, but a lot of people in IMDs do not have family members or advocates looking out for their best interests. Seriously mentally ill people often get pushed along a conveyor belt of sub-par treatment and decisions that are convenient for the providers rather than their patients.

Because of political-correctness taking over the whole mental health care system, providers rarely even refer to a person with SMI as a "patient." At some point, they started referring to them as "consumers." That struck me as a bizarre adaptation of a word understood to describe people who buy things, as in "consumer spending for the holidays." Seriously mentally ill people, disabled and subsisting on a meager stipend from the government, are not "consumers," unless this is a sick, ironic inside joke. It reminds me of Henry Kissinger when he once referred to the elderly as "useless eaters." I call people living in the IMD or the Board and Care "residents." If they are in a hospital or in relation to some other medical setting, they are a "patient," a more accurate description based on their situation or needs. The Orwellian doublespeak gets even more bizarre, such as with the new trend of referring to people with criminal records as being "justice-involved." Do these euphemisms help anyone? I find it appalling. We change words to reduce stigma, but not the circumstances which create stigma in the first place. Why are the outpatient clinics called "Behavioral Health" when we're dealing with a neurological disease of the brain?

After three months in the IMD, I asked what dosage of Clozapine Noah was on. That he was even on it at all was a miracle and it all started four months before when he was at the Transitional IMD. I happened to be there on the day when the psychiatrist called Noah into his office. I asked if I could sit in on the session and Noah agreed. Not a whole lot was discussed between the two and Noah sometimes just tells a psychiatrist whether or not he is sleeping well or if he has other side effects like drooling or constipation. Sitting in on a few dozen psychiatric sessions, I never witnessed much or any dialogue regarding symptoms, such as visual or auditory hallucinations. I mentioned to the psychiatrist, in front of Noah, he was still experiencing "positive symptoms." I used that language because it implies sustained delusions and hallucinations. "Negative symptoms" describe things like having low energy, lack of empathy, lack of concentration, and disinterest in personal hygiene.

Generally speaking, we know in the medical world when someone is "positive" for a disease that is a bad thing. With schizophrenia, the "positive" symptoms are considered worse. Although, when we look at both positive and negative symptoms of schizophrenia, it may be a toss-up which symptoms are worse. This may sound preposterous, but some people hear voices and still manage to compartmentalize their symptoms and function almost normally in other areas. I don't know if it has anything to do with people who are more left-brain dominant than right-brain dominant, but that would be an interesting case study on its own.

I remember once reading posts on a website regarding anti-psychotics. People on these medications would give honest reviews and experiences. At that time, my son was taking a certain medication and doing very poorly on it. As I read through all the posts about this one medication, I saw a theme; the men wrote they did horribly on this drug, it didn't help them and even made some worse. In contrast, most women posted comments that it worked well for them, with one lady saying that as soon as she went on this particular medication, she felt like taking a bath and cleaning her house! Different drugs impact different genders differently and I've yet to meet one mental health care professional who seemed to know that.

I asked the IMD psychiatrist at the temporary IMD if we could try Clozapine. He was surprised Noah was not on it and assumed it had already been tried. What separates Clozapine from all the other anti-psychotics is the potential for the white blood cell count to drop dangerously low. Weekly blood tests are needed to monitor the white blood cell count and after six months, they can taper off into monthly blood draws. With enough passing years, they can reduce the frequency of the blood tests even further.

Clozapine is known as the best anti-psychotic for most people with schizophrenia, although there is a small percentage who cannot tolerate it. In rare cases, it can be life-threatening. One friend had her son try clozapine in a hospital setting under close observation; he didn't do well and was taken off it, remaining in the hospital until he recovered from the side effects. In more recent years, doctors and therapists have advocated for using Clozapine as the first one to try, instead of the last one. The reasons for opting to start with other medications may have something to do with the risks involved, but it may also have to do with patient compliance.

Having the blood draws weekly could be difficult to manage, especially depending on a person's living accommodations and access to proper care. It is probably more expensive than other types of medication management because of the need for frequent blood tests, so insurance companies make the patient try other medications first. This is just another example of money and business taking priority over what is best for the patient. Ultimately, it is a short-sighted, money-wasting approach. A patient who gets better faster is probably less expensive in the long run. Just dealing with insurance companies alone is enough to raise your blood pressure.

Studies have shown that Clozapine works best when it can address positive symptoms as soon as possible. If a person waits a decade to try it, like Noah, the results may not be as noticeable. I had one of those "moments" with Noah, where I felt I could reason with him and took the opportunity to tell him "now is a perfect time to try Clozapine." I meant it. He was in a locked facility where we could guarantee he would be monitored closely. We could guarantee that if he had any concerning side effects he would be just steps away from the nurses' station. We would not have to go to a lab, schedule appointments, and wait around. He could have his blood drawn right at the IMD. When I relayed all this to Noah, he simply agreed to try it, after so many years of saying no. For years he said he was afraid of needles and didn't want his blood drawn. Once again I got a surreal response, where he said he was no longer afraid to have his blood drawn because it makes him "feel clean." What I didn't share with Noah was that I would be very interested in seeing his response to Clozapine, knowing for sure he would not have access to street drugs or alcohol. If he took anything else, it would be harder if not impossible to know if the Clozapine was a superior medication or not.

He started on the Clozapine before I knew he would be discharged a month later and fortunately, they kept the prescription going at the longer-term IMD. After three months at the second IMD, they still had him at the same low, initial dosage. He was not even at the therapeutic level yet. It was hard to get ahold of the new psychiatrist, Dr. Agravarian, who oversaw the residents at the second IMD. I didn't take it personally because the state of affairs is that psychiatrists who work for these IMD's and county mental health clinics are known for not returning phone calls. I'm sure if payment was coming directly from me the phone calls would be returned.

It is unnerving to know that psychiatrists can prescribe medications with no physical examination whatsoever. Many don't think it is necessary to speak with family members to get background information and a history of a person's mental illness. And it gets even worse! Many of the older psychiatrists were taught that mental illness is an outgrowth of anti-social behavior and not a pre-disposed, genetically based brain illness. They may have negative attitudes and prejudices against family members, especially the mother. Many decades ago, there was a term, the "schizophrenogenic mother," used to insinuate that a cold, unaffectionate mother who was simultaneously over-protective, made her child succumb to schizophrenia.

The National Alliance on Mental Illness (NAMI) has spent decades countering this inaccurate assumption of causation. And now the world of psychiatry agrees there is no evidence to prove such a dysfunctional dynamic in a family can cause mental illness. Certainly, schizophrenia would be more common if that were true. One of the only comforting things Dr. Harris said to us when Noah was only 17 was *schizophrenia is not caused by bad parenting.* A certain percentage of the population is genetically predisposed to this brain illness and many other factors come into play for it to emerge. This can include nutritional deficiencies or complications during the mother's pregnancy, stress during formative childhood development, and teenage cannabis use. The whole subject of cannabis is a real conflict for families who see its use indirectly or directly undermine the stability of their loved one. We recognize that cannabis and CBD oil have impressive therapeutic benefits for some, but for people with mental illness, it usually makes matters much worse.

When I got ahold of Dr. Agravarian, he was surprised I would suggest the Clozapine dosage be raised. Did I offend his authority? Did he believe a dosage that low was sufficient? He answered by saying Noah reported he was feeling well and he did not have any hallucinations. Noah confided in me more than once that he was still having hallucinations and he also confided the same to a peer coach who visited and called him sporadically. While I didn't say what I thought, I wanted to ask Dr. Agravarian if he realized his patients lie to him for both rational and irrational reasons. One would think it goes with the territory, that a psychiatrist may not get the most accurate input when it comes directly from a person with a thought disorder. Dr. Agravarian would not promise me he would raise the Clozapine. He condescendingly said he would look into it. Days later, I was complaining in-person to a nurse that the Clozapine dosage was too low and that the psychiatrist did not seem cooperative. The nurse listened with interest, but she was not in any position to change the situation. This conversation was overheard by the Program Director who stepped out of her office and asked if she could help. I explained to her I wanted to see if Noah could improve further on a higher dose of Clozapine and she was surprisingly sympathetic and pro-active. She admitted that all the patients on Clozapine do better than others who are not on it.

What kind of grand experiment is going on then, when others are not being offered the best medication for treatment at a therapeutic level? Without diving into a conspiratorial rant that will make you question my sanity, let it be known the government has experimented on unsuspecting citizens in the past and likely continues to do so. Dr. Robert Heath of Tulane University experimented on forty-two patients with schizophrenia and prisoners in the Louisiana State Penitentiary, all funded by the U.S. Army. The good doctor dosed them with LSD and bulbocapnine and implanted electrodes into the septal area of the brain to stimulate it and take electroencephalography (EEG), readings. Various experiments were performed on people with schizophrenia who were stable, other experiments were performed on people with their first episode of psychosis. Some were given methylphenidate to see what it did to their minds. Other government agencies in the United States have admitted to doing mind control experiments without permission and the awareness of individuals from larger sections of the population. The CIA is notorious for conducting these types of covert experiments in conjunction with hospitals, prisons, and universities. I sometimes lament whether or not my son was tapped for any "experimental" case studies on anti-psychotic medications. Look up the Tuskegee Syphilis Experiment if you doubt these things happen. Research "Project MK Ultra" and learn how unethical and illegal some of the CIA's activities are since their inception, preying on innocent people, even with fatal outcomes. This is not conspiracy theory, rather historical fact. The United States Commission on CIA Activities within the United States was set up in 1975 by President Gerald Ford to investigate it. Do we believe these covert programs ended? Interestingly, a common fear of the paranoid schizophrenic is the government is spying on them. We can all laugh nervously now that Edward Snowden has confirmed it!

Fortunately, the Program Director persuaded Dr. Agravarian to increase the Clozapine for Noah. At the next quarterly progress meeting, the staff noted Noah was participating more in their programs. His increased participation was in sync with the increase in medication. I pointed this correlation out for the staff and they all assumed a sheepish grin. After that experience, I realized I needed to be more pro-active about Noah's medication management. While he continued to get better, consistent with regular intervals of increasing the Clozapine, I can't say the difference was like night and day. The difference was more like night and early morning. Noah had a little more interest in other people, their feelings, and verbalized more about what went on around him. He was more relaxed and content, as opposed to doped up and sluggish.

One of the unique features of Clozapine is a patient can experience gradual improvements for over a year after starting it. After reading through some of Dr. Robert Laitman's research papers, as well as other studies he referenced, compelling findings suggest that people who are put on Clozapine close to the onset of their first psychotic episode can have a remarkably positive outcome, compared to waiting years later. There is now a growing consensus among psychiatrists to start patients on Clozapine sooner than later. After years of being contrary and rebellious, Noah now seemed more open to suggestions. That said, Noah still lived in a locked facility, which prevented him from making most of the bad decisions he made before.

Did the Clozapine help Noah stop hearing voices? The answer is no, but I think they may have lessened. If a schizophrenic person doesn't confide about the voices outright, another way to know is in how a person interacts with others. Imagine how disruptive it would be if we heard an imaginary person talking to us while trying to carry on a conversation with a real person simultaneously. Noah told me once he sees a little girl sitting on his bed and he has to leave the room several times before she disappears. I can only imagine this; it must feel like an overlap of the dream state while awake. For some, the only way to escape the voices is through sleep. Noah now had a little more energy to go places and do things, so this had to be a sign the voices subsided a little.

I was informed that "hearing voices" is not the worst of all the schizophrenic-positive symptoms. I suppose if the voices are not saying mean things or suggesting violence, the person could ignore them. Who knows? Maybe hearing voices is not as debilitating as feeling like lead bricks are attached to your feet. Noah went through one phase where he said he could barely keep his eyes open; he felt they were glued shut. This was another of his symptoms, which those around him, less sympathetic, considered a manipulation tactic.

Of course, a person is more than just their illness. But based on my observations of my son, he seems to experience just about everything through the filter of schizophrenia. One of my more interesting observations is that I believe he experiences time differently; many people do. As we age, it's a common experience among people that time appears to pass ever more quickly. Time may go by more quickly when we return from a journey as compared to starting. Feelings of anticipation might subjectively alter our experience of time. Children often experience short periods as excruciatingly long, due in part because of immaturity while learning to handle delayed gratification. I remember as a child that summer vacation seemed to pass slowly, with my schoolmates noticeably bigger upon their return to the fall semester. As older adults, a whole year can seem to pass in the blink of an eye.

Because Noah never complains of boredom while having nothing to do, I think he must experience time more quickly than others. Many people with schizophrenia feel overwhelmed by stimulating environments like a shopping center and the pace at which other people move and talk. They struggle with the simple activities of daily living like bathing and brushing their teeth. Often so preoccupied with their inner world, they may accomplish little in a day but still feel rushed and needing to be alone. Aside from being very internal, feeling overwhelmed can also come partly from the brain's struggle to regulate multiple environmental sensory influences. This is referred to as "gating" and Clozapine helps with this problem more than other medications. We take for granted that when we are focused on what we want to focus on, other sensory influences recede. If you experienced all surrounding sounds and visual stimuli equally, it would be hard to carry on a conversation or focus on one activity without interruptions and distractions from all other sensory input.

Another form of stress for schizophrenics is the inability to read people's emotions as expressed through facial expressions or voice. This is a critical problem for people with autism as well. Sometimes this happens between people from different cultures, but for most of us, by the time we are children, we can recognize happiness, sadness, anger, fear, or a myriad of other emotions expressed through the face or tone of voice. The inability to interpret facial features or tone of voice could understandably cause anxiety or even paranoia for anyone. It's a primal part of our being, to fear what we don't understand. This has also heightened problems in law enforcement interactions with the mentally ill; they may see a police officer as a monster ready to attack. As an aside, one police officer told me after I did a CIT presentation that a high percentage of people rescued from the L.A. River during rainstorms are those with autism. They tend to be fascinated by water, even in unsafe situations.

FOURTEEN:

The 11th Hour

Noah was discharged from the second IMD exactly a year after he arrived. He was not yet participating in all the programs, but they felt he made as much progress as he could. Either that or some other financial incentive generated the discharge plan. As is the case with many people exiting a locked facility, the next "step down" in the level of care is an open facility with extra support. The term "Step Down" program has also gone out of favor and was replaced with "Enhanced Residential" care to describe the next phase of the mental health care maze in California. So many euphemisms and acronyms, it makes my head spin. Enhanced Residential care means: an open Board and Care with an assigned therapist and case manager through the Assisted Outpatient Treatment (AOT) program. Sometimes they are called EOP's, which stands for Enhanced Out-patient Program. They each meet with their client weekly and try to help the person maintain medication compliance, sobriety if relevant, in a coordinated effort to prevent relapse.

The IMD assured me that if Noah faltered hard within thirty days of being in an open residential program, they would re-admit him to a locked facility. Noah moved into an Enhanced Residential Board and Care in October 2018 and was assigned a case manager and psychiatrist who I never met. I did meet his therapist toward the end of his stay, as we finalized paperwork for him to be discharged.

More ludicrous, bureaucratic obstacles were thrown at us, such as the Enhanced Board and Care's refusal to order enough medication to see him through the following month while in transition and before a new psychiatrist took over and prescribed. This would have allowed some leeway for Noah to settle into his new accommodations without having to rush to see yet another new psychiatrist. That alone can cause tremendous stress. If there is a way to make things difficult, the broken mental health care system knows how to do it expertly. One other time when Noah was in between Board and Care facilities and psychiatrists, I managed to get his GP doctor to authorize a refill on his prescriptions since the previous psychiatrist refused to.

While living in this "Enhanced" program, Noah had little to do all day and was not accountable to hardly anyone. He was there for five months and his routine included smoking thirty cigarettes per day and eating at fast-food restaurants. I never asked him if he had started panhandling again because I didn't want to know. He met weekly with the therapist and I didn't see much progress. He again went for long stretches without showering. Noah only had seven outfits to wear. Staff kept promising they would help Noah with his laundry, but it never happened. His clothes were laundered only twice over the five months when I took the clothes home to wash them myself. They didn't care how filthy he was, living at his "Enhanced" program with a weekly therapist, psychiatrist, and case manager. There I was again, "Helicopter Mom Extraordinaire," because I had no confidence in what the staff was doing with him or for him.

For decades there have been debates about whether "cognitive behavioral therapy" or any therapy can help a person with schizophrenia. Some believe they just need consistent companionship and assistance to do ordinary things like laundry or problem-solve on day-to-day basic needs. Some therapists believe cognitive therapy can be very useful to people with schizophrenia, but they are denied by insurance companies who do not want to pay for the comprehensive level this type of illness requires. Similarly, Medi-Cal will not pay for a deep cleaning dental procedure, but they will pay to pull a rotten tooth out. They will pay for emergency care, but not preventative care.

I began to worry about what the next housing situation would be and I knew that it would just be another Board and Care, with no support or supervision creating a high chance for total relapse. Noah would once again spend his days panhandling for extra money to buy street drugs or a dangerous amount of caffeine, undermining his medications. This may sound like an exaggeration, but it's possible to have a heart attack from too much caffeine. One time he gave himself a migraine from it and asked to go to the hospital. At the Board and Cares, they often only serve coffee in the morning, but residents find ways to drink it all day. At one of the Board and Cares, Noah's roommate poured lukewarm water from the bathroom sink into a mug with what looked like a half cup of powdered instant coffee. He slurped it down like mud.

There would be nothing for Noah to do, nothing to engage his intellect, and no motivation to maintain any meaningful social skills. Worse, he would probably return to such a state of instability, the cycle of property damage and evictions would begin again. Once again, I would face the challenge of whether or not I could maintain a relationship with my only son. All of it was a crying shame after everything Noah had been through, including homelessness and the toll of two years of hospitalization. One would think the government would seek ways to optimize the financial return on their investment, to better ensure relapse is not so likely. I'm not sure why, but the Department of Mental Health sent me a copy of the bill they paid for his five-month hospital stay; it was for $100,000. I can't imagine what the costs were for the following two IMD placements spanning 20 months. Some business model!

I began meeting with other mothers who had sons with schizophrenia. What could we do with our sons, when the mental health care system failed us all so predictably for so many years? Many parents watch their adult children cycle through Board and Care evictions, unsuccessful attempts to live at home, hospitalizations, locked facilities, bouts of homelessness, and even jail. Voluntary programs like FSP and AOT can help while they last, but they are not designed to go on indefinitely. Political activity, awareness, and advocacy end up being natural progressions as we parents search for answers and accountability. We find out there are funds available for our sick family members, but somehow just beyond reach because of illogical restrictions and even stigma inside the mental health care field, a place where you least expect it.

One time I was standing in line at the post office and the lady in front of me moved forward as a business card fell out of her pocket. I picked it up and saw she had an important title within the Department of Mental Health. Does anything happen by accident? I must have said something out loud like, "How ironic," as she turned around and we began a conversation. I told her I was very frustrated with how slow things move within certain mental health agencies, even waiting weeks to get a phone call returned. This woman told me she was retired but validated my suspicions in confirming that some government employees work slowly on purpose. I asked why and she said that if they worked too efficiently they would be out of a job! She then told me to call her anytime I needed help.

Many physical disabilities are permanent and it is well understood in the medical community that a person with certain physical or developmental disabilities needs assistance and services *for the rest of their life*. With mental illness, there is a major blind spot with some providers and agencies. Public programs available to those who cannot afford superlative private care require the "consumer" taper off of services when they appear to do better. These are the same professionals who are bewildered when a person with schizophrenia wants to go off their medication.

No doubt, mental health care providers who are more than competent and dedicated must experience equal frustration, aware of the lack of continuum and inevitable relapse with their clients. Reading *Breakdown: A Clinician's Experience in a Broken System of Emergency Psychiatry* by Lynn Nanos, was a real eye-opener. As a mobile emergency psychiatric social worker, Ms. Nanos' book details the frequency in which her professional recommendations are subverted once she gets the patient admitted to a hospital. She saw many of the same people over and over again, watching the Mental-Health Industrial Complex's vicious cycle play out ad nauseam.

I joined this small group of mothers with schizophrenic sons who met regularly to share our collective ideas on how to create a holistic and truly therapeutic environment for our sick family members. We wanted to borrow from all the private programs we knew that work or have the potential to work. We discussed how to raise private funds or grants and see if we could create a pilot program to gain support and maybe even partial funds from DMH, the Department of Mental Health. Around this time, DMH and the L.A. County Board of Supervisors researched the licensed Board and Care system in a way they either had never done before or at least not in a long time. The lengthy and comprehensive report came out in 2019 and I got to read through it since I was on the email list of a city official appointed to the L.A. County Health Commission.

The report revealed the county in a state of emergency with so many Board and Cares closing. The ones still open teetered on the edge of closing because of a lack of funds. The report included the actual budget for several Board and Cares, including ones I knew. The Board and Cares need *twice* as much funding as they receive to stay in business. These Board and Cares take in about $1,000 per month from each resident, the total of their monthly, federally funded SSI benefits. Do the math and you will realize that it costs more per day to board your dog in a kennel than what SSI covers daily for a human being.

I do what I can in terms of advocacy and sharing information, signing petitions, and attending conferences. After a while, it all seems like "Ground Hog Day" with the same discussions and surveys taking place for decades. While there is some improvement in advocating for the seriously mentally ill, the homeless population keeps getting larger. Efforts are made to "patch up the dam" but the dam is still breaking. Many local governments, by necessity, prioritize the crisis as a socio-economic issue, over one of the main causes: mental illness. Many of my NAMI friends, moms with ill adult children, know the fight is almost hopeless, but we soldier on praying our efforts will not be in vain. Some of us have given up on the very organizations which were supposed to represent the needs of family members or the most seriously mentally ill in our society. Instead, these organizations are catering to higher functioning "peers" or as mental illness advocate DJ Jaffe refers to as "the worried well." We used to assume the mentally ill were only a small portion of the homeless population, but they make up a large percentage and they are often drug-addicted to complicate the mess.

It's gotten to that point where we have to distinguish between "mild or episodic mental illness" and chronic "*serious* mental illness." When you have wealthy celebrities talk about their mental illness, it's all sexy and acceptable. But when the subject of NIMBYISM (Not in My Backyard) comes up or helping people who don't know they need help, then it becomes very controversial. If a celebrity graces the cover of a magazine and discusses their bouts with depression or anxiety, the public rallies around that beloved person and wishes them well. That famous person also has the money to get the best of private care. Sometimes, even the tabloids leave the person in peace for a while. When it comes to the unknown homeless, psychotic person who has just set up a tent a block from some nice neighborhood, the residents are in an uproar about how to get these desperate people out of sight and out of mind as quickly as possible. The mentally ill homeless are open to constant attacks, from human and non-human predators, off medication, and on-street drugs, all while searching for basic needs such as food, cigarettes, or a pair of socks. Not much healing goes on in that situation.

As each month passed with my son in this "step down" Enhanced Residential program, I became more anxious about where he would be placed next. I knew his time in the program would evaporate soon. I somewhat "enjoyed," if I can use that word, the reprieve I had with him being either in a hospital or IMD for two years. With my son in locked facilities, I slept at night, knowing he was not likely to be harmed and could not go missing. Though not impossible, I also knew it was unlikely he had access to any street drugs while in an IMD. Lest anyone think drug trafficking does not take place inside of locked facilities, of course, it does, just like in jails. I could not even bring Noah homemade food when visiting.

It's just difficult. Any outside food had to be wrapped or sealed from the restaurant or market it came from, so no one could bring in drug-laced food.

FIFTEEN:

Light at the End
of the Tunnel

Shortly after the New Year began in 2019, I forced myself to make a vital phone call. Noah had been on the waiting list for three years, for an opportunity to live at the John Henry Foundation. A truly therapeutic, long-term residential program in Southern California, the Foundation has existed since the 1980s. It is privately funded by the family members whose loved ones live there; that's one reason they are so successful with residents. They have the funds, the wisdom, and the excellent staff-to-resident ratio to make significant improvements in the lives of the mentally ill people who live there. The John Henry Foundation is one of the few role models I know of for ideal housing and treatment. The little group of moms I joined aspired to re-create something approaching the John Henry Foundation with the help of grants, public and private funding. Each year, L.A. County receives close to a billion-dollar budget to work with for the mentally ill, but the services provided all have to be voluntary. Some of those funds go to support the FSP and AOT programs. Were someone to set up their housing for a small group of people, they would need to support the residents with the FSP or AOT programs, if allowed.

The housing model the moms brainstormed over would be a voluntary program too. We did not know if our sons would live in a program we had planned for them, but we knew for sure they didn't like living in the typical state-licensed Board and Care with crappy food and nothing to do all day. I'm reminded of the saying about one definition of insanity: doing the same thing over and over but expecting a different result. In the world of mental health care, the same mistakes and oversights are made continuously, which is crazy-making for all.

Fortunately, the John Henry Foundation is drastically different. They have space for forty-two adults, many of whom can have their own bedroom. They choose each resident carefully and the prospective resident must agree to follow the rules and the program they offer. They do not want anyone living there against their will or not compliant with the programs and activities. They provide activities the residents enjoy, including shopping excursions and visits to coffee shops. Some of the more active residents appreciate the other outings, which include trips to the beach, movies, concerts, miniature golf, and local zoos. They also choose prospective residents carefully so they will merge into the existing John Henry Foundation population with as few risks as possible. One of their goals is to encourage residents to form real friendships. If they think someone will not get along with others or upset those already living there, then it is not a good fit.

Now, a fair question is, why would a person with no insight into their illness agree to all the rules? Perhaps it has to do with the fact the John Henry Foundation is objectively a nice, clean, cozy-looking place to live. Many people invited to interview have come directly from hospitals, locked facilities or the horrible Board and Cares I have described. It's not such a hard sell, to those who come from terrifying situations in the most crime-ridden areas of the city. Perhaps those who agree to abide by the rules don't understand what they commit to, but every step of the way they are encouraged to keep up. Residents are spoken to with kindness and respect and their self-esteem is pumped up daily with compliments and support for anything positive they do.

When I called the John Henry Foundation in early 2019, I expected to be told Noah was still on the waiting list and it would be a while before they had an opening. They don't have a lot of openings because the residents are stable and allowed to live there as long as they want. I was elated when the Clinical Director said they would have an opening in about a month and Noah should visit in a couple of weeks to interview. I was excited and nervous, hopeful, and also dreading the day when we had our interview. Of all the different rules for living at the John Henry Foundation, the one rule I was nervous about is their policy for residents to smoke no more than eight times per day. That is eight cigarettes total, compared to the thirty to forty cigarettes Noah had gone back to smoking in his "Enhanced Residential" Board and Care. To my surprise, Noah agreed to this smoking policy! Manna from Heaven!

I'm not a religious person, but I couldn't help feeling there was divine intervention that created this situation where Noah was open to making sacrifices to live there. He did see with his own eyes the environment was more appealing than any other place he had lived since his illness began. This included a community room with computers and guitars for the residents. They have since added a piano and ping-pong table. At the John Henry Foundation, a cluster of well-maintained cottages surrounds a grassy courtyard with shaded patio coverings and patio furniture for lounging. They have pet cats that both staff and residents care for and raised flower beds for gardening. The overall environment is appealing and well maintained.

Instead of wanting to get out of there as quickly as possible, as with the standard Board and Care, the place has wholesome, tranquil energy where anyone can relax. It's a great place to live or visit.

Bedrooms are clean with new furniture. The common areas in each cottage have leather couches, TV, and cable access. Bathrooms are spotless. They serve healthy food at the John Henry Foundation, prepared by a professional chef; sugary desserts are only allowed on special occasions and they have many residents on special diets, designed by their nutritionist. At the John Henry Foundation, they understand how important good nutrition is for both physical and mental health. They also celebrate every holiday, with treats and decorations and holiday gifts for the residents.

Another part of the program involves exercise five days a week. This is good for anyone, but especially for people who need to have more energy, as the medications are otherwise sedating. My son, and everyone who lives there, needs a lot of structure and their program has the perfect balance of activities, including opportunities for outings seven days per week. They actively help residents with their "ADL's" which stands for Activities of Daily Living. This includes showering, changing clothes, and all things related to personal hygiene and medication. It can include other simple tasks such as doing their laundry.

I don't want to sound like an infomercial for the John Henry Foundation, but it is important for anyone reading this, whether they are a family member or a mental health provider, to know what is necessary to give a person a chance for recovery. There is no One-Size-Fits-All approach, but what they do involves a personal connection with each resident, honoring their level of functionality and gently inspiring the person to do as much as they are capable of. They have a psychiatrist from a respected university who makes weekly visits to the residents. The psychiatrist is even willing to visit residents in their cottage or bedroom if that is more comfortable for them. He is a stark contrast to virtually all the other psychiatrists Noah had encountered to date. There are even family meetings where the psychiatrist is often a guest speaker, to answer questions.

For many people, they get the support they need to learn how to manage their money and banking, how to use transportation, and get back into college or some form of employment if they are capable. For my son, who quickly established himself as an excellent musician, they are inspiring him to play his guitar outside and serenade other residents. He was never shy before when he performed in front of others, so this is a goal we all have for him.

Getting Noah situated at the John Henry Foundation was not easy for a different and unexpected reason. While Noah agreed to move there and follow all their rules, the Public Guardian responded by saying they would not authorize a move out of the county. It was surreal to hear those words from the conservator when the John Henry Foundation would be the absolute best place for Noah, by a long shot. How could they sabotage his best chance for recovery? By "recovery" I am not inferring there is a cure for schizophrenia. I use the word "recovery" to indicate: stability, higher-functionality, and having our ill loved one more content and satisfied with their own life, making real steady progress.

Conservatorships are granted for the entire state and in our case California. Moving to an adjacent county would mean the Public Guardian conservator would have to drive an extra thirty minutes to make quarterly visits. Other duties of the Public Guardian may have been strained by the extra distance, but they did not ask if I could assist. This request, to share the responsibilities of the conservatorship, would not have been considered far-fetched; just a couple years prior, there was a discussion at a NAMI-sponsored Conservatorship Coaching seminar about the proposition to allow parents to be co-Conservators with the L.A. Public Guardian. In the same way, you can have more than one Trustee for a Special Needs Trust, the co-conservator could reduce some of the burdens on the Public Guardian with their excessive caseloads and allow family members to be more involved in the decision-making process.

The only way to get around this legal obstacle was for me to take over as the conservator. This was a responsibility I did not want initially. Noah was conserved by the Public Guardian for over two years and they made many mistakes, including negligence with his SSI benefits, which caused the SSI to be canceled until I got it re-instated. The Public Guardian agreed to facilitate me becoming the conservator quickly and they set up an emergency court hearing so that could happen, the one time they moved with speed and efficiency! A few weeks later I became the conservator and I didn't have too much stress after the fact since I knew Noah would be going to a great residential program. My duties as a conservator would be much easier now than any of the previous years when Noah was so symptomatic and non-compliant. Even a Conservator cannot mandate treatment when the mental health care system does not have enough staff or funding or when their loved one is unapproachable.

I was cautiously optimistic when Noah agreed to the structured program offered at the John Henry Foundation. He committed to morning meetings with the whole group. He committed to thirty minutes of exercise Mondays through Fridays. He committed to participating in on-site and off-site activities, and he committed to smoking much less. Both his father and I showed up for this interview, so I think Noah understood it was a big deal and we were united in our desire for him to live there.

SIXTEEN:

Ron

Five days before Noah got accepted to live at the John Henry Foundation, something shocking happened. It was a Sunday evening, and ironically I had spent most of the day at a mental health advocacy-training seminar. I came home, after having been gone for about five hours, to find a three-page letter on the kitchen table. In that letter, Ron my boyfriend of nearly ten years told me why he had to leave me. His letter was full of unwarranted hostility, but as I read the letter I knew he had to rationalize why he would leave me at all, and why he would leave in such a sneaky way. He also took our beloved golden retriever Nutmeg, justifying it, as she had become his emotional support dog. Indeed, he went almost nowhere without her. But I realized once she was gone, she had been my unofficial emotional support dog for the last six years as well! The dog had been my regular source of comfort for so many years, and yet it didn't register until she was gone.

Ron was a tortured soul in so many ways; I should not have been surprised that our relationship didn't last or that he would leave me one day without warning. As much as I have driven home the point mental illness is genetically based, Ron was a textbook example of how child abuse can create mental illness as well. He didn't have to have schizophrenia to hear voices in his head. He hears a constant loop of his mother's negative diatribes, reminding him daily what a failure he is. With two parents who were alcoholics, Ron's chances of becoming one were 100%. It's more the norm than the exception for people who work in the mental health field to have been directly impacted by mental illness or dysfunctional families. Who else can relate to or empathize with such tragedies?

When I met Ron, he had been sober for over a decade. He had also quit smoking, using the same Twelve Step Approach. Both addictions were conquered with his first round of the Twelve Step Programs, unlike many others who relapse before they can achieve long term success. Even though Ron has many aspects to his personality which seemed injured and frail, other aspects of his personality seemed strong as steel to me. He was a real survivor in more ways than one.

One bone of contention between Ron and his older sister Judy was that she became critical of him over the years for choosing a career that did not pay well: case management. Their father had four degrees and was a bio-nuclear engineer; it was easy for her to sit and judge. She never worked herself, damaged goods as well, but with a husband who supported her financially. Ron always felt Judy was in denial about what happened to them as children, whereas he more obviously tried to understand mental illness, personally and professionally. He tried to heal himself by being in an environment where he felt he could make a difference in someone's life. These were aspects to Ron's heart and soul that endeared him to me.

I wasn't oblivious to Ron's psychological struggles, but I was so drained from Noah that I had little energy left to pamper Ron. For the times when I did try to be his mental health advocate, I was rebuffed. One time I suggested he go back to 12-Step meetings and he told me he was too anxious to go. Only in retrospect, as I re-live many situations with Ron in my mind, have I come to realize he was incapable of being in a mature, trusting relationship, let alone take on the role of a being a part-time step-father. Based on the chronic and severe abuse inflicted upon him by his mother, it is amazing he didn't turn out to be just as violent as she was. That said, how could he ever love a woman in a balanced way, with that kind of fundamental betrayal by his mother from birth? Ron was so consumed with his anxiety and shame, he barely had the energy for any candid discussions with me how he felt about our relationship. I don't think Ron wanted me to know how deeply depressed he was, but it became more and more obvious each passing year we were together. During the span of our relationship, I did have thoughts more than once about how I might react if I found Ron dead one day, having committed suicide. Toward the end, I felt like I was running a Board and Care, with one resident: Ron. Because of his chronic physical and psychological pain, he was sleeping or at least laying down twelve hours a day, usually holding an ice pack to his back after walking the dog.

In his letter to me, Ron said my gesture to hire a lawyer to ensure he got disability coverage was an affront to his capabilities to handle his affairs. Unknowingly, he took that as criticism instead of my commitment to support him. He projected onto me all his mother's criticisms that she hurled at him. She became Ron's inner voice. This was an insane woman who told Ron that President John F. Kennedy was killed because Ron was a "bad little boy." How's that for a guilt-trip? This was the same insane woman who made her three children sit on their knees all night, without the ability to use the bathroom, while she screamed at them for hours. The kids found temporary refuge at school, but to say they did not have an adequate home life to study and do homework is an understatement. More than once, Ron and his sisters had to witness Mabel trying to hang herself in the shower. At Mabel's funeral, the priest had a hard time getting anyone to stand up and say anything nice about her.

Ron struggled to make good grades even with his Attention Deficit Disorder. It had to have been related to his constant state of high anxiety. I had seen many fragile aspects to Ron's psyche and I knew why, listening to one sad childhood story after the next. At some point between applying for the disability benefits and when he got the approval notice, Ron decided to leave me and keep it a secret until the day he left. Just by the wording in his letter, it seemed written in haste. I did go into shock that day, to find him and the dog gone. My body shook for hours and I didn't sleep for two days straight. He only took bare essentials and left me with almost everything he moved into my home eight years prior; his whole apartment of possessions and furnishings, mostly overflowing in the cluttered den that became his Man Cave.

He only left that day with what he could lift without injuring his back further and what he could fit into the bed of his Dodge truck. He must have rushed around the house in a panic to load up the truck before I returned. He even left a thirty-pound bag of dog food, useless to me since he took Nutmeg with him. In his letter, he accused me of being judgmental and he said he just wanted to be alone. Well, since I am not a saint, I can say I did have judgments and opinions and certainly worries about Ron's mental stability; I kept most of those impressions to myself. I was constantly trying to bolster his self-esteem and act like things were normal between us, for his sake, when they were not. I thought I was affording him a haven to live without worries over money. Ironically, he was the one sitting in judgment of me, to the extent he felt he could no longer accept my flaws, the way I accepted him. What hurt the most in his letter was the insistence I was mishandling Noah. He claimed it would surely lead him to become even more psychotic, more destructive, and more sociopathic. He warned me he saw a real risk of my son murdering me one day!

Ron was mortally offended I could not follow all his professional advice. He thought Noah's rebellious behavior would not end unless I stopped taking him out to lunch, stopped buying him things, stopped visiting him in the hospital, and that I should even consider disowning him. I kept this thought to myself, but honestly, sometimes his rigid attitude struck me as a "mean streak" he may have inherited from his mother! Ron felt the only way Noah would change his behavior (as if he had control over his schizophrenia) was if I withheld the only thing I could reliably offer my son: the demonstration of unconditional love and support. When I talk with people living successfully with schizophrenia, their common stories emphasize loved ones who never gave up on them, a vital component to their recovery.

One of the most gut-wrenching stories of unconditional love and resolve comes from Cynthia and Anthony Hernandez of Chino, California. Their son Aaron, who has paranoid schizophrenia, had also been denied the care he needed for many years, with revolving door hospitalizations and many warning signs of what could happen. In 2014, Aaron snapped and inflicted nearly fatal stab wounds on both parents and killed their family dog. Surviving the violent assault, his parents amazingly continued to advocate on Aaron's behalf almost immediately after he went to jail. Later, the Hernandez couple traveled around the country advocating for better preventative mental health care. They teamed up with former Rep. Tim Murphy to support his reform bill called the Helping Families in Mental Health Crisis Act, which was signed into law, just before President Obama left office, as part of the 21st Century Cures Act. This legislation helps bring more funding to evidence-based treatment programs for the seriously mentally ill (like AOT), and also created the first-ever position for a President-appointed Assistant Secretary for Mental Health and Substance Abuse Disorders.

Ron saw me as a "pushover," a willfully co-dependent enabler. But I did put my foot down on many issues. Ron saw me turn over the responsibilities of Noah's housing and case management to professionals. He saw me allow Noah to be homeless, long enough to realize that Noah was not going to have an epiphany or insight into his illness. I thought that was a pretty extreme demonstration of "tough love" but I guess Ron saw that as too little, too late.

Ron also saw me give away powers to the Public Guardian and distance myself from some pretty crucial decision-making, for Noah to understand his actions had brought me to the point of exhaustion; I was so worn out I could not help him.

Friends of mine were surprised Ron left me and not the other way around. Friends were also surprised I was not furious enough about him taking our dog Nutmeg to hire a private investigator, to hunt him down and get the dog back. But this is a man who has been suicidal. The last thing I needed was to feel like I did anything to push him over the edge and take his life. I had to let go and let go fast because I have learned through so many other life lessons, that hanging onto resentment only hurts me more. The end of my relationship with Ron happened the same week Noah and I started a new beginning, a new lease on life. I decided quickly to focus on that and not the sad ending. I do wonder how Ron would react if he knew Noah made quick and substantial improvements after moving to the John Henry Foundation.

My house seemed too big for me without Ron and our beloved dog Nutmeg. I first purged out all of Ron's personal belongings and then did my spring-cleaning. I got rid of many things I no longer needed or could identify with. I also gave to charity many things I had hung onto, in the hopes that one day Noah would have his own apartment and I could help him furnish it. If that day ever comes, we'll get him all new things! I hired a contractor for house repairs in preparation to rent it out. I knew I would eventually find a new place to live without the memories and reminders of all our struggles in that house.

Noah started to do so well, from Day One, at the John Henry Foundation, that I decided to move sooner than later. I knew I could make some passive income by renting out the house and also move a little closer to Noah. It struck me as a win/win situation. There were other benefits to moving, not the least of which are the objective facts I moved to a safer, cleaner, and prettier city where I could heal, recuperate and have more energy for myself and my son. The only drawback to the move was that I would not be as close to friends and my local NAMI support system. I made a promise to myself to seek out the NAMI chapters in my new area. I had to have faith in the Creator this was the right decision, so while my home of seventeen years was undergoing long-overdue repairs, I started searching for a house to rent much closer to Noah's new residence.

There were unexpected expenses and a few other obstacles to get through, but at least during the transition, Noah was well taken care of for the first time in thirteen years. I cannot speak highly enough of the residential program Noah is in and it serves as a realistic model for recovery. The entire nation's mental health care system could take its cues from its program. I know there must be some other wonderful programs that get similarly good results and provide stability for their residents, but to say we don't have nearly enough of these places is a huge understatement. Aside from not being served in an ideal way, according to Mental Illness Policy Advocate DJ Jaffe, 50% of the seriously mentally ill in the United States are not being treated *at all*. This was the statistical fact in 2017 when his important book, *Insane Consequences,* was published.

I don't know how long Noah will be at the John Henry Foundation. I hope he agrees to live by their rules and do so happily for as long as he needs to be there. I hope he gains some insight into how the structure of their days and the activities they provide are assisting him in recovery, higher functionality, and more personal satisfaction in his own life. He certainly looks better, healthier, and more vibrant.

We've had some small hurdles to get through since he arrived but the staff handled them quickly and to everyone's satisfaction. He is doing well there, with a glimpse of the "old Noah" emerging, at least in his smiles, which had been absent for years. He's playing his guitar more and catching up on more than a decade of technology advances on a laptop.

SEVENTEEN:

Coping

I'm sure that in the long run, it is more cost-effective to take care of mentally ill people and use preventative measures rather than let these folks fall through the cracks and then wind up in the criminal justice system or perpetual need of emergency services. Government officials need to factor in the costs of revolving door hospitalizations, law enforcement, the court system, public defenders, public nuisance abatement, and other services which would be unnecessary if SMI people were provided with compassionate and competent care from the beginning.

As I write these words, there is a global pandemic (COVID-19), which has finally made many in government wake up to the additional serious threat to public health posed by so many homeless people, most of whom have a mental illness. They can contract and spread disease just like anyone else, but they don't have the "luxury" to "shelter in place" or even understand the importance of doing so. If the love of humanity is not enough to motivate the Powers-That-Be to do the right thing, then we can still look at the economic toll as a motivator to do a better job in helping those with serious mental illness.

One angle I have *not* seen included in studies on mental health care costs is the emotional and economic toll it takes on family members who are the caretakers, sacrificing their livelihoods to take care of their ill relative. One hundred percent of all involved family members become depressed with their loved one's plight and on-going crises. Some family members get through it better than others and many are moved to advocacy as a result. What is advocacy? A mental health advocate participates in activities, even initiates activities, which look into how mental health agencies and officials can improve conditions for the mentally ill.

Advocacy work can be on a local, county, state, regional, or national level; I hope this memoir has an impact on all those levels. When advocates discover anywhere in the mental health care system where laws or policies can be improved, or if we uncover some waste, fraud, or discrimination, action must be taken. One person can make a difference and many people create great change. An advocate works on behalf of someone else, to right the wrongs.

I have always used a compulsion to work in my own business as a coping mechanism and got involved in local advocacy as well. Some family members become physically and emotionally paralyzed by stress. An honest look at the toll of mental illness on society should include what happens to family members, even if we just look at it from a financial perspective; loss in productivity, and loss in tax revenue. Many caretakers must leave work and cancel other important obligations to tend to our sick loved ones. I have often referred to myself as an unpaid social worker. Perhaps a silver lining in a post-global pandemic world will be a better understanding of how we all impact each other so profoundly.

I even have conflicted feelings with regards to other mom-friends, dealing with their out of control, unstable adult son or daughter. Some of my friends are retired, so they can devote more time and energy to working on behalf of their ill adult child who is now in their thirties, forties, or even older. *Caring for a mentally ill family member never ends, no matter what dreams you might have for your future.*

While operating my own business during every crisis, I have been consulting with a client countless times, only to hear my cell phone ring inside my purse. I maintain my composure, even when I know some upsetting message could be waiting for me and as soon as I break away to check my messages. That said, I have felt sorry for my retired friends. They should be enjoying their retirement, hanging out and relaxing, pursuing other interests, traveling, and playing with grandchildren. Instead, they are visiting jails or hospitals, and have their own health issues to deal with, including cancer. Parents must come to terms with the fact we don't have responsible, accomplished adult children who we can rely on when our own health fails. You can imagine the dread we go through on holidays, especially Mother's or Father's days.

Everything in this memoir is true; only the names of some individuals and places have been changed, to protect the innocent and the guilty. Our story is certainly not over, but I am glad that my son is now on a good path to functional recovery and stability. However, it would be naïve for me to assume we will never see another hospitalization again or that Noah will never relapse. The good news is the high quality of loving and professional care he now receives will reduce those chances enormously. The program he is in now also indirectly heals me and validates a parent's intuition.

Family members who read this memoir might be at a different stage with their loved one. They may have been shaking their heads while reading familiar stories that they have experienced as well. Some of our struggles are so common they are cliché. Even though the emergence of mental illness in the family is highly emotional and disruptive, spreading awareness about schizophrenia and the current health care policies can help us all move in the right direction for better treatment, management, coping, and even possibly a cure one day.

Caretakers, be they a family member or a professional health care provider, can create their own appropriate "flow chart" of what they can anticipate will happen on the trajectory of this mental illness. If there is a history of mental illness in the family tree, then you have been forewarned and should be on the lookout for its manifestations. Despite misguided campaigns to prevent mental illness, it really cannot be prevented any more than one can prevent the pre-determined genetic coding for the color of one's eyes. There is a predisposition to mental illness that cannot be denied.

Once the illness begins to manifest, our "flow chart" of likely outcomes and actions will be determined, based on whether our ill loved one has insight into their illness or not. Here the flow chart splits in half, going in opposite directions because the trajectory will be quite different. This one feature alone will determine the level of cooperation and commitment a person with SMI will have in managing their illness or accepting help from others. One can have the best resources in the world, but if the ill individual is not willing to cooperate, there is a limit to what you can do to help. At the very least, your ability to help will be delayed.

Of course, there are some people with no insight who are cooperative, but I venture to say when there is no insight into the illness, we see more often a resistance to treatment which can last months or even years. Some people with no insight have strong enough family bonds they may cooperate, even when they don't think they are ill. If that is your loved one, consider yourself lucky, because it is not the norm. As Dr. E. Fuller Torrey notes in his book, *Surviving Schizophrenia*, the prognosis will be influenced by how early the illness began, whether the person lives in a rural or urban environment, and whether male or female. You are correct to assume the prognosis is better when the onset is later in life, when the person lives in a rural environment and when the person is female. Additionally, schizophrenia is a spectrum of illnesses, affecting different parts of the brain and some are destined to be higher functioning than others.

If your loved one becomes ill as a minor, you have a lot more power to control their road to recovery including medication compliance, although the prognosis can be more troubling for a minor, compared to someone older and therefore further along in their brain development. The male brain does not finish developing until age 25! Just don't make the same mistake I made, which was to send my son away to a residential high school program where they eventually revealed how ill-equipped they were to handle serious mental illness in an adolescent.

Another way the flow chart to stability is seriously impacted is if your loved one has a dual diagnosis. Anyone who self-medicates with illegal or harmful recreational drugs is going to complicate, delay, or even seriously sabotage their potential for insight and cooperation. Additionally, street drugs and alcohol will simply interfere with the medications. Even heavy tobacco use will speed up the metabolism of medication and make it necessary for doctors to prescribe a higher dose, with the expected increase in side effects. You will become an expert in a dizzying array of anti-psychotics, anxiety and mood stabilizers with names such as Seroquel, Lamictal, Geodon, Haldol, Lithium, Risperidone, Abilify, Latuda, Depakote, Zyprexa, Clozapine, and others. Your loved one may easily be on a combination of antipsychotics, as well as anti-depressants. Like a ping-pong ball, you will feel batted back and forth with guilt between public arguments stating people are violent when they are on psychotropic drugs versus those who say people become violent when they are *not* on their meds.

Another branch of your flow chart is determined based on what kind of public mental health care resources you have in your community. Even with a willing patient, if there is a lack of housing options, therapists, and treatment programs, you may have to rely heavily or exclusively on private options. The private options may or may not exist in your community, so the flow chart continues to be defined based on what you can afford and who is available for hire. Many mothers I came to know in my local NAMI chapter were justifiably fed up with the lack of therapeutic housing available for a person who doesn't need to be in a locked facility but also cannot live safely on their own or with the minuscule supervision provided by the typical state-licensed Board and Care. Depending on the family's finances, the Board and Care route should be enhanced with extra therapies, nutritional supplementation, and activities generally not provided by the Board and Care. Otherwise, in my opinion, there is a high chance for relapse or at least no progress, judging by the current Board and Cares I have visited and where Noah lived.

Family members should immediately seek out their closest local NAMI chapter for educational classes and family support meetings. I procrastinated in getting involved with a support group for a long time, partly due to being in denial and partly due to ignorance. It's hard to juggle the demands of your ordinary life, with the extraordinary demands of mental illness in the family. I couldn't comprehend how serious this was in the beginning. Some of the milestones in understanding the severity of our situation have come with each revision of my Will and Noah's Special Needs Trust. The Trustee of the Special Needs Trust is often a parent with a successor Trustee named for when the Trustee passes away or becomes incapable of fulfilling their duties. The Special Needs Trust can also pay professional caretakers who will oversee housing and living expenses, medical, personal, and social needs.

Every concerned parent has to think about financial futures; another thing that keeps us up at night. Who will care for our children when we go? Every important decision I have made since my son became ill has been filtered through a Litmus Test of how the decision will affect Noah as well as me. I wanted to move out of state years ago, but could not possibly do that without having a stable son to take with me. Nor would I take him to a place without competent mental health care options. That certainly narrows the choices! I have long understood that I not only need to financially support him for the rest of *my* life but also the rest of *his* life.

The rules of the Social Security Administration for granting SSI (Supplemental Security Income) benefits include the rule the recipient cannot have more than $2,000.00 to their name (as of 2020). If a person on SSI benefits has more than $2,000.00 attached to their social security number, federal government benefits stop. It is a case where the person with SMI has to live in abject poverty to get this minimal financial assistance, which only covers food and rent in a Board and Care and nothing else. If the SMI person lives outside of a Board and Care, such as with family, the benefits get reduced to $650.00. Again, caretakers are punished for taking on more responsibilities and expenses.

The SSI beneficiary does get a token amount of money to spend as they wish, which is called PNI (Personal Needs Income). To date, it is around $130.00 per month and does not go far. Many people with SMI spend the entire monthly allowance on cigarettes and junk food. The main portion of the SSI benefit (@ $1,000) must only be used for food and shelter. If someone were to give the SSI recipient X amount in additional dollars to help support them, that money would get deducted from their SSI benefit the following month as it is considered a "resource."

By having a Special Needs Trust, the beneficiary can have other necessities paid for, by and in the name of the Trust, instead of gifted outright to the person. This is one way to protect the person's SSI eligibility and it is perfectly legal. Every parent should educate themselves about having a Special Needs Trust for their ill son or daughter, a crucial move if they have any assets which their son or daughter stands to inherit. I have a couple of friends who do not have any significant assets to will their children, but they have taken out Life Insurance policies, which can fund the Special Needs Trust when they die.

People have to make the right decisions for their circumstances. I chose to name a private professional fiduciary to be Noah's successor Trustee. If any person named as a Trustee does not want to fulfill the obligation, they can name someone else or turn it over to the courts to hire someone. There are even pooled Special Needs Trusts, like one called Proxy Parents, where the SNT is handled by a committee.

Some choose to hire an attorney or even a bank to be the Trustee. My only word of caution is to avoid hiring any bank that would pay itself a percentage of the Trust Fund assets instead of an hourly rate for management services. If a bank compensates itself each year with a percentage of the Trust's worth, it is a conflict of interest when it comes to decisions for expenditures on behalf of the beneficiary. They might hold onto the assets for their bottom line instead of disbursing funds for the beneficiary.

In good faith, many people think the best choice is to have a sibling or other family member named as the Trustee. This places quite a burden on someone who may want to remain an emotional support system for their brother or sister and not have to hold the purse strings. It could create resentment with a relative and it can also be a time-consuming job. Trustees can pay themselves out of the Trust, but then again it could be stressful for a relative to feel like they took away funds from a disabled family member. The Trustee should understand how the mental health care system works so they can protect assets and make wiser choices for the beneficiary. One friend initially nominated a family friend, who was a professional accountant, to be the Trustee for her son's SNT. While being good with money matters is always a bonus, this same man was uneducated in the mental health care system and the rules regarding SSI benefits. The accountant made critical mistakes, and then abruptly died. No successor Trustee was listed to take over and finding another qualified Trustee created extra stress.

Currently, I wear "three hats." I am my son's Representative Payee for his SSI benefits, I'm his Conservator, and I am the Trustee of his Special Needs Trust. These departments all need to be organized and files kept indefinitely. Parents will want to keep long term all the records related to treatment, hospitalization, and medications for future reference and legal documentation.

Support groups are one of the more reliable ways you can meet other family members, some of whom are much further along in the process. They can help provide answers and resources. As you lose some of your former friends who distance themselves from your family tragedy, you will find new friends with something profound in common. Family support groups can also be a good way to meet other parents if you want to create your own housing "co-op" as an alternative to the state-licensed Board and Care system. I spoke with one woman who went through all the legal requirements to turn her own home into a licensed Board and Care. There are pros and cons to being state-licensed. You may get extra funding, but you also have to abide by certain laws that could undermine your program policies and goals. For example, a state-licensed program is legally obligated to give the SSI recipient their full PNI (personal needs income) to do with what they want. The federal government is not concerned with how your loved one spends that money. They may be spending it on drugs, which would undermine your whole program of recovery. In a non-licensed program, you could create a reward system and other incentives for the patient to learn how to handle their finances more wisely.

Another recommendation I have for family members is to take opportunities (when you are not in the middle of a crisis), to educate yourself about things related to mental illness, even if you don't think you will ever use those services. Use me as an example, I started attending meetings about how to get your loved one conserved, even when I thought our chances were very remote. Several years later, when I had an opportunity to get my son conserved, I already knew exactly what to do and who to call for back-up support. You know the saying "Hope for the best, but plan for the worst." I recommend family caretakers become "mental illness preppers."

It could be necessary, even for a normally high-functioning person with a career and financial assets, to be conserved. That person might need to be supervised and in a locked facility, if for no other reason than to get them stable on their medication and have them regain some insight into their illness. We could say entertainer Britney Spears is one of the most highly functioning and high profile people in the world, who still, as of this writing, is conserved by her family, years after a very public mental break-down. More times than not, the conservatorship is for a much more disabled person, with no assets or ability to regain any sense of stability within a relatively short time.

Unless sent to a forensic hospital because the patient has committed a crime, most IMD stays last from six to eighteen months. In 2016, a person needing to be in an IMD in Los Angeles County could wait anywhere from five to twelve months or more to get into one. The hospitals initiating the conservatorship end up warehousing the individual because they cannot release them if it has been determined they need to be in an IMD. The conservator, whether it ends up being the Public Guardian or a family member, has the power to approve or reject (within reason) where the conserved person gets transferred.

It's funny how parents are often viewed as the "enemy" in many mental health care decisions, but when it comes to them being the conservator, the system heartily approves. It's one less person the county has to keep track of (and pay for associated costs). I figured I would take over as Conservator if I was unhappy with the Public Guardian's handling of Noah's case. I assumed they had more resources and knowledge about how things work all down the line. What I later learned was that Noah's Public Guardian was new to her job and had to consult with a supervisor on many decisions. Months would go by before she returned any of my phone calls, so I finally resorted to calling her supervisor who was quick to respond.

The special kind of conservatorship used for the seriously mentally ill is called an LPS Conservatorship. The initials LPS stand for the attorneys, (Lanterman-Petris-Short) who created this type of legal guardianship, which needs to be renewed every twelve months. Some people are conserved for just a year or a few years. Other people are conserved for many years. It all depends on a combination of need to be conserved in conjunction with whether or not the conserved person (called the "conservatee") continues to agree to the arrangement. They do have a say in the matter! It is difficult to get the conservatorship in place to begin with; so many family members do not want to let it expire too soon once they have it in place for their loved one. The only way to get the application for conservatorship, (without having to do it privately and with a lot of expense), is to get your loved one hospitalized. With the laws being what they are, it is hard to get a person with mental illness hospitalized, so right from the get-go conservatorship seems remote and unlikely, even for many who desperately need it. This is one point I drive home when I speak before law enforcement. I want them to know when they authorize the 5150 hold, there could easily be a mom like me, grateful for another opportunity to get our loved one conserved. I convey to the officers that from a parent's perspective, it is never a waste of time to get our ill relative into a hospital. This is because, unfortunately, we usually have to "build a case" for the imperative need to get them conserved. If a person with SMI was hospitalized ten, twenty, or more times, we might be able to finally "shame" the hospital into opening up a conservatorship.

With current laws throughout the United States, a person must be defined as "gravely ill" or an imminent "danger to self or others," before the police or mental health care workers can authorize the 72-hour hold (called 5150 in California). Imagine what it would be like if a person could not receive medical care until they were "gravely ill" or in 4th stage cancer! "Danger to self or others" is a bit subjective. Fortunately, with the passage of Laura's Law, and others like it in other states, a person's previous mental health history has to be taken into consideration. There isn't always someone available to provide that "previous history" but at least Laura's Law is moving advocacy in the right direction.

With previous history taken into consideration, it sets in motion the ability to implement Assisted Outpatient Treatment (AOT). **Laura's Law** is a California state law that allows for court-ordered assisted outpatient treatment. To qualify for the program, the individual must have a serious mental illness plus a recent history of psychiatric hospitalizations, jail, threats or attempts at violence towards self or others. This law was named after Laura Wilcox, a receptionist who was killed by a man who refused psychiatric treatment. It was modeled on Kendra's Law, a similar statute enacted in New York. In a real life example, if the police are called to evaluate a person acting psychotic and the person appears calm and rational when interviewed, they still have to consider the person's mental health history if provided to them by any family member or concerned party.

When AOT does outreach to the person, if they continually refuse to cooperate with the outreach personnel, AOT can obtain a court-order for treatment. Many of the people do comply once they feel the law has mandated they get treatment. It's referred to as the "Black-Robe" effect. Additionally, a conservator has the legal right to summon the police and mandate they authorize the 5150 72-hour hold. In other words, the conservator is not at the mercy of inexperienced PET team social workers to make sure they get their loved one hospitalized.

No matter whether you live in a large or small community, it behooves you to get acquainted with people in charge at these various mental health care agencies and departments. Show up at their offices, shake their hand and make eye contact. Don't be intimidated by anyone. Speak to them privately when they appear at conferences you attend. At the end of the day, these are just people too and there is even a good chance they got into the mental health care field due to one of their own family members being ill. Being polite and calm on the phone, even when it is the tenth time you have called, can go a long way in getting what you want. If the person on the phone is genuinely helpful, tell them that they have "made your day" or call them your "hero." They will be even more open to assisting you in the future. There are also on-line social media groups you can join in order to get more informed about mental health policies, petitions you can sign and other forms of advocacy. Look at the list provided in the final pages of this book for websites and groups to align yourself with.

At a certain juncture, our "flow chart" may go haywire. The truth is we don't have control over everything that happens. We must accept this truth, but also trust that circumstances can suddenly change for the better, sometimes in the most seemingly random ways. Some of the best outcomes in our personal family flow chart appeared by chance. Eventually, there may be less choice available, such as when my son made it nearly impossible for him to be housed anywhere. In retrospect, I should not have been so shocked when he ended up homeless. But even in the more dire situations, including incarceration, there can be people in the system who can help re-direct your loved one to more appropriate placement. It requires a parent or other caretaker to be tenacious. The squeaky wheel gets the grease. A well-known NAMI adage is, "we will never give up hope."

All along the way, if there is an opportunity for your ill loved one to feel like they are making good choices and participating in their own recovery, they should be supported and congratulated and feel like they have a say in their own life. This is difficult and yet some people with SMI have to make a lot of bad choices before they come around to the wisdom in trying something new and accepting help from others.

As the aging process takes its toll, my best years physically and professionally are surely behind me. For both of us and in our relationship, I am reserving space in my heart for our best years that I hope are yet to come. With advances in technology and medical breakthroughs, I am hopeful Noah will continue to progress and have opportunities that I can hardly imagine now. He has never been more receptive to the advice and suggestions of those around him.

Each person deals with schizophrenia in their family in their own way. Some people cope through advocacy and activism. Even when our situation seemed completely hopeless, I still felt genuine satisfaction in trying to help other family members find solutions and benefit from our experiences. I have also gotten a lot of satisfaction being involved in the Crisis Intervention Training program for law enforcement. Just knowing that some of the things I have told police officers will make a difference in how they handle an unstable person in crisis has made me feel useful beyond words. Some family members eventually understand the importance and wisdom of self-care, even when it may appear to be selfish or indulgent to themselves or others. I have been able to blow off a considerable amount of steam, by expressing myself through the written word. This is how I try to make sense of it all. I write; therefore I am.

Everyone has their own spiritual interpretation of why mental illness manifests in our lives and how we can grow from it. I still consider my son to be one of my greatest teachers, with profound spiritual lessons learned that could not have happened any other way. I confess that as a teenager, I practiced yoga and meditation in order to get a natural high. I thought this alone was a doorway to higher consciousness, but the range and flexibility of my higher consciousness was not truly tested until my son fell apart. Sure, I had other intense moments in life and disappointments, including a failed marriage. I did not, however, question my relationship and karma with another person more than with my son and what it meant for both of us. It's easy to feel spiritual when life goes your way and success seems magical, but when everything comes unglued, the real test of faith, humility and the struggle to not be bitter all move to center stage.

For the atheists and agnostics dealing with their loved one's mental anguish, I understand your pain and the void as well. My own concept of God is very abstract and I have accepted my own belief that the Creator is incomprehensible. God, for me, is not a humanistic personality who we can call on for personal favors or for explanations. Nevertheless, I have had many other-worldly and spiritual experiences, which have confirmed for me that there is an order to the Universe as well as an afterlife.

About nine months before Noah was accepted to the John Henry Foundation, I met with a small group of eight people for an in-person session with a famous psychic-medium. I was only drawn to this opportunity because a good friend had just spoken to this medium and was astounded with how accurate he was. Prior to this, I would have dismissed psychics as being mostly unreliable and overly confident in their active imaginations. But this is also something that desperate and forlorn family members do. We search for answers, even in the most unconventional ways, such as with psychics, faith healers and astrologers.

This psychic-medium did not know me from Adam. I don't even think he knew my name as his assistant made all the scheduling and payment arrangements. When he turned to me in the room, the first thing he said was, "Who is Vita?" Well, that was my mother's name. She passed away when Noah was only ten years old. I was pretty amazed he got such an unusual name so clearly from this other dimension. He went on to say that she is very concerned about Noah. The psychic-medium got an image of a nurse's hat and said that my mother knows her grandson is in some kind of hospital and he has addictions and a psychological problem. At the time, my son was in an IMD and I was just starting to meet with other NAMI moms about what kind of housing we could create together. I knew Noah was going to be discharged eventually and there were no good options for him within the public mental health care system. I feared he would just be dumped at another Board and Care. As I said nothing and provided no clues, through the medium, she told me she knew I was worried about where he would live next.

Through the medium, my mother told me that with her and my father, it's "all hands on deck," meaning the both of them on the Other Side were trying to help Noah and lead us to a good, therapeutic place for him to live. My mother also communicated through the psychic-medium that I would write another book, but a book not like the other three I had written. That was also true; I had just started this memoir. There were many other things revealed through the psychic-medium that brought chills up my spine, things no one else could possibly know. Before concluding the session with all eight of us, where the psychic-medium was astoundingly 100% accurate with everyone in the room, he asked me if I had any more questions for him. I asked him if he could connect with someone who did not voluntarily come forward to communicate with me and he said yes. I asked him if he could bring forward my boyfriend Ron's deceased mother.

As soon as the words left my mouth, he leaned back and said, "Oh, I just got this taste of alcohol in my mouth. She was quite a drinker wasn't she?" Well, he had certainly identified Ron's mother Mabel, for sure. He then said, "She was kind of a Joan Crawford type, yes?" Of course that comparison was spot on as well. The psychic-medium then paused to choose his words carefully, "I don't want to say there is an actual Hell, but let's just say she is in a lower dimension right now and really needs to work on herself."

This, along with other experiences, made me feel there is no death, life is eternal, and we are all connected souls. It was gratifying to sense my own deceased parents aware of our struggles and wanting to help when the laws of the universe permitted it. It was also striking to know that there was such an accessible cosmic link between Ron's mother and me; I had never even met her.

I might be deluding myself, to cope, but even when we are starring in a movie we don't want to be in, I believe the roles we play have a higher purpose. I believe Noah and I chose each other in this lifetime; we chose to be mother and son. We were meant to travel this road together and I believe there is a God-given reason for why everything happens.

Glossary for Common Terms Used in Mental Health

(with editorial comments by author)

ADL (Activities of Daily Living): (ADL) Activities of daily living are routine activities people do every day without assistance. Medical and mental health providers list six basic **ADLs**: eating, bathing, getting dressed, toileting, transferring, and continence. Mental health workers regularly evaluate the functionality, stability, and progress of a patient by tracking the ADLs. Many seriously mentally ill people struggle with their ADLs, especially in the area of personal hygiene. Inability to do these activities of daily living can also count as "negative" symptoms of schizophrenia.

Anosognosia: This term refers to "lack of insight," a symptom of severe mental illness that impairs a person's ability to understand and perceive his or her illness. It is the most common reason why people with schizophrenia or bipolar disorder refuse medications or treatment. Anosognosia is a borrowed word from medical terminology, now used commonly in a mental illness context for meaning lack of awareness about having an illness. Someone could have anosognosia regarding a physical disorder that is obvious or clinically evident, such as paralysis of a limb. There are also differing opinions about whether or not someone with anosognosia will always lack insight or if that can change.

I have personally seen instances where a person appeared to have insight into their illness when stable on medication and then lose that insight when off their medication. I have also seen people who lacked insight into their illness even when on medication.

Antipsychotic medications: Antipsychotic medications are used as short or long-term treatments for bipolar disorder or schizophrenia to control psychotic symptoms. Those symptoms can include hallucinations, delusions, or manic behaviors. Some antipsychotics also treat depression and some medications have shown they can prevent future episodes of mania or depression.

Antipsychotics are used "off label" as well, in smaller doses to be used as sedatives, for insomnia, anxiety, and/or agitation. Antipsychotics may also be used with mood stabilizers. Antipsychotic drugs help regulate brain functions that control thinking, mood, and perception. It is still not clear exactly how these drugs work.

Medications used to treat schizophrenia and bipolar disorder include, by brand name: Abilify, Saphris, Vraylar, Clozaril, Lamictal, Latuda, Zyprexa, Depakote, Seroquel, Risperdal, and Geodon. The newer antipsychotics can act quickly and help people avoid the high risk and impulsive behaviors associated with mania. More rational thinking often is restored within a few weeks. For people with schizophrenia, there is greater variance in their efficacy and this is one reason why it can take much longer to find the right medication or combination of medications for the individual.

For some, consistent use of antipsychotic medications can make the difference between a person living independently and being able to work or not. For others, the use of antipsychotic medication only appears to improve symptoms but not eliminate them completely.

There has not been enough research to make any conclusive statements, but some people are using CBD oil in high doses in order to control both positive and negative symptoms of schizophrenia. This is also controversial since the psychoactive ingredient in cannabis can be responsible for triggering psychosis, especially with a still developing brain in adolescents. Most people with schizophrenia have a worsening of both positive and negative symptoms when they use cannabis.

Anxiety: Anxiety is an emotional state that can be caused by an event or disturbing activity that makes a person nervous and they may feel they are on high alert much of the time. Anxiety can be a reaction to stress, but it can also occur in people who have had no obvious trauma to cause it. Anxiety can contribute to physical symptoms in addition to mental stress. Anxiety can be mild or severe.

When chronic anxiety is paired with depression or post-traumatic stress disorder, it can be very disabling.

(AOT) Assisted Outpatient Treatment: This law is also known as "Laura's Law," passed by the California Legislature in 2002 as AB1421. It allows for court ordered outpatient treatment for a person with a mental illness who meets certain legal criteria. Other states in the United States have similar court-ordered treatment programs that go by other names, but with similar goals.

Bipolar Disorder: Bipolar Disorder is a mental condition marked by alternating periods of elation in mood and depression. This disorder used to be called Manic Depression. Bipolar Disorder 1 and Bipolar Disorder 2 make the distinction between the more severe manic episodes of Type 1 and the less severe (hypomanic) episodes of Type 2.

Borderline Personality Disorder: Often noted as BPD, this mental health disorder impacts the way you think and feel about yourself and others. It causes problems with self-image, difficulty managing emotions and behavior, and a difficulty in maintaining healthy relationships. Some are convinced that borderline personality disorder (BPD) affects females more than males. BPD has been identified in a higher percentage of people who were adopted, have experienced sexual abuse and who are referred to as "cutters."

A "cutter person" attempts non-suicidal self-injury. It's defined as the deliberate, self-inflicted destruction of body tissue. Cutters aren't trying to kill themselves; they self-harm to feel alive. There is some kind of endorphin release when engaging in this risky behavior.

Board and Care: A Board and Care home is a licensed 24-hour care facility. These can be senior living homes offering room, board, round the clock staffing, and assistance with bathing, dressing, medication management and other forms of personal care. A **Board and Care for Mentally Ill Adults** will accept adults ages 18-59 who are ambulatory and do not have any serious physical handicaps, but need supervision and medication management for their mental illness.

Most Board and Cares for the Mentally Ill have a visiting psychiatrist and some also provide other medical services or transportation to medical appointments. Some Board and Cares have recreational activities and on-site programs. Others provide voluntary off-site day programs.

Clinical Depression: Depression is a mood disorder that causes a persistent feeling of sadness and apathy. Also called major depressive disorder or clinical depression, it affects how a person feels, thinks and behaves which can lead to a variety of emotional and physical problems. The depressed person may have trouble doing normal day-to-day activities, and feel suicidal.

More than just a bout of the blues, depression isn't a character weakness, rather a chemical brain imbalance. Depression may require long-term treatment. Most people with depression feel better with medication, psychotherapy or both. Well-meaning people who try to lift the spirits of a depressed person by reminding them of what they have to be grateful for could make the depressed person feel worse. Sometimes it helps to let depressed people express themselves; just show sympathy and acknowledge their feelings.

Conservatorship: A legal contract which names a guardian or a protector, appointed by a judge to manage the financial affairs and/or daily life of another due to physical or mental limitations, or old age. A person under conservatorship is a "conservatee," a term that can refer to an adult since children with parents as legal guardians are not conserved. The **LPS Conservatorship** is specific to mental illness cases and it needs to be renewed on a yearly basis. For this type of conservatorship, the conservator has the final say in where the conservatee is housed and what medications they take.

The conservator can also dictate who the conservatee may associate with it. For example, if the conservator feels that a certain friend or relative could be a bad influence, they can prevent that person from speaking with or spending time with the conservatee. A conservatee often relinquishes their driving privileges during the conservatorship.

Crisis Intervention Team/ Crisis Intervention Training: A Crisis Intervention Team (CIT) is a police sponsored mental health collaborative program. The term "CIT" is used to describe a law enforcement training program with the goal to help improve interactions between law enforcement and those living with a mental illness.

The National Alliance on Mental Illness (NAMI) has instigated many Crisis Intervention Team (CIT) programs as local initiatives designed to improve the way law enforcement and the community respond to people experiencing a mental health crisis.

Dual Diagnosis: Dual diagnosis (also referred to as co-occurring disorders) is a term for when someone experiences a mental illness and a substance use disorder simultaneously and it does not matter which disorder manifests first. People experiencing a mental health condition may resort to alcohol or other drugs as a form of self-medication to mask the mental health symptoms they experience. However, research and common sense shows that self-medicating through alcohol and other drugs worsen the symptoms of mental illnesses.

When someone has more than one diagnosis, such as schizophrenia as well as a mood disorder, the primary diagnosis is called "Axis 1" and the secondary diagnosis "Axis 2."

What mental health advocates have to be very careful with, in regards to their loved one with SMI, is to not *over-emphasize* the substance abuse component. Otherwise, the SMI person may get routed into a drug cessation program without the adjunct of mental health services.

Full Service Partnership: Adult Full Service Partnership (FSP) programs are designed for adults between 26-59 years of age who have been diagnosed with a severe mental illness and would benefit from an intensive service program.

I don't know how much the FSP programs are tailored to the individual, but my son was assigned a therapist and case manager who he saw weekly. He also saw a psychiatrist monthly who provided a little talk therapy. **TAY-FSP** is the same program for younger adults from age 18-25. TAY stands for Transitional Age Youth. The Department of Mental Health in each community contracts with the FSP agencies.

At the time of this writing, FSP and AOT programs are not covered by private insurance. Funds come from a variety of different sources for each state that have these programs. In California, some of the funding comes from Proposition 63, the Mental Health Services Act, which passed in 2004.

IMD (Institute of Mental Disease): An institution for mental disease is defined as any "hospital, nursing facility, or other institution of more than 16 beds, that is primarily engaged in providing diagnosis, treatment, or care of persons with mental diseases. These are not the same as the Mental Institutions or "Insane Asylums" from centuries past.

IMDs are long term care psychiatric facilities, licensed by the State Department of Health Care Services (DHS) and/or the State Department of Mental Health (DMH). They are contracted to provide care for persons who no longer meet criteria for "acute care" but are not clinically ready to live in a board and care facility or to live independently. The current IMD would be referred to as "sub-acute" and they usually treat a person for six months to two years.

In some instances where a patient does not improve in one IMD over a year or more, they may get transferred to another IMD to see if a different treatment team can have a more positive impact. Most IMDs are similar in their programs and approaches, so it is not like they are drastically different. Shifting a patient to another IMD can be an admission that they don't feel they can help the person make any more improvements, but the patient is not ready to live independently or in an open facility.

Mood disorder: A mood disorder is a mental health problem that primarily affects a person's emotional state. It is a disorder in which a person experiences long periods of extreme happiness, extreme sadness, or both. When the person experiences both extreme ends of the mood spectrum, it is likely diagnosed as Bipolar Disorder.

Obsessive Compulsive Disorder: Obsessive Compulsive Disorder is a personality disorder characterized by excessive orderliness, perfectionism, attention to details, and a need to control one's environment and other people. There are so many manifestations of OCD that there are too many to list here. Some of them are comparatively benign, such as excessive hand washing or constantly checking for locked doors, to the more serious compulsions that truly interrupt a person from living a productive, satisfying life. Some "workaholics" rationalize their OCD by the positive results of their dedication to their job or career. But other areas of their life may suffer such as health or relationships. There is even a relatively new addition to the list of classic OCD behaviors, to include orthorexia, which is the unhealthy obsession with eating healthy. Excessive dependence on technology and social media has created a whole new generation and type of OCD behaviors in people.

Prognosis: A prognosis forecasts the likely course of a disease or ailment. People often confuse the terms prognosis and diagnosis. The difference between the two is that while a prognosis is a guesstimate as to the outcome of treatment, a diagnosis identifies the problem and gives it a name, such as depression or obsessive-compulsive disorder.

The prognosis for people with schizophrenia depends on many factors including medication compliance, treatment, and other physical health components, as well as family support or the lack of it. If a person has optimal support for a long time, their positive symptoms, namely hallucinations, may lessen in older age.

Psychosis: A severe mental disorder where thought and emotions are so impaired that contact is lost with external reality. Psychosis may manifest "organically" without any obvious cause, but can also be triggered by drug or alcohol abuse.

Representative Payee: A representative payee is an individual or an organization appointed by the Social Security Administration in the United States. The payee receives directly the Supplemental Security Income or SSI benefits for anyone who can't manage his or her finances. A special SSI-Rep Payee account is set up for direct deposit of the monthly benefits. The Rep Payee then makes payments from the Rep Payee account on the behalf of the SSI beneficiary.

The amount of the benefits received depends on the housing accommodations for the beneficiary. Generally speaking, maximum benefits are allotted to a person living in a licensed Board and Care and the Board and Care accepts that maximum amount as payment in full for room and board.

SSI recipients who live with a relative or any location that is not licensed will not receive the maximum benefits. This is based on an assumption that a person living outside a Board and Care must have someone else contributing to their food and shelter needs. However, this punishes the person or family who is taking on the financial burden of housing and feeding the disabled person. Additionally, a mentally ill homeless person who qualifies for SSI benefits could certainly make good use of the maximum allowable benefits for obvious reasons.

Schizophrenia: Schizophrenia, a long-term mental disorder involving a breakdown in the relation between thought, emotion, and behavior, which leads to faulty perceptions, inappropriate actions and feelings. Withdrawal from reality and personal relationships, the person with schizophrenia suffers from delusions and hallucinations which are highly disruptive to normal functioning.

SMI (serious mental illness): Serious mental illness (SMI) is defined as a mental, behavioral, or emotional disorder which results in serious functional impairment, substantially interfering with or limiting one or more major life activities. There are forces presently at work to establish schizophrenia as a brain illness and not a "behavioral" disorder, in order to help de-stigmatize it and allow for more research and funding.

Because of the current political climate, mental illness advocates now have to distinguish the differences between moderate or episodic mental illness versus chronic, serious mental illness. Advocates know that funds meant to serve those with SMI are often delegated to those who are not seriously mentally ill. This discrimination has been going on for a long time and only changes in the law will turn the tide in making people with SMI a priority.

SSI (Supplemental Security Income): *Supplemental Security Income (SSI)* is a Federal *income supplement* program funded by general tax revenues (not *Social Security* taxes). SSI is designed to help aged, blind, and disabled people, who have little or no income. It's intended to meet basic needs for food and shelter. Mental illness candidates can qualify if they have never worked and paid taxes. Some people get accepted for SSI benefits easily while others are denied and need to appeal the process.

SSDI (Social Security Disability Income): Those with mental illness can receive SSDI income if they ever worked and paid taxes. SSDI recipients also qualify for Medicare as opposed to Medicaid. There is currently one way in which a person who has never worked can qualify for SSDI. If the mentally ill person became ill as a minor (with documentation), they can switch from SSI to SSDI once one of their parents starts to draw upon their own retirement benefits.

After being on SSDI for two years, the person with SMI can qualify for Medicare (years before they would otherwise qualify for it as a senior). This is one of the main motivators to get onto SSDI, since Medicare is considered better insurance coverage than Medicaid.

Special Needs Trust: A Special Needs Trust is a legal document and contractual arrangement, where a fiduciary relationship allows a physically or mentally disabled person to receive income without sacrificing their eligibility for SSI, Medicare or Medicaid. In fact, if a person has disability benefits and insurance and then receives an inheritance, they will have to pay back Medicare or Medicaid unless the inheritance is protected in the form of a Special Needs Trust.

In a fiduciary relationship, a person, committee or an organization act on behalf of the beneficiary to manage their assets. There are first-party Special Needs Trusts, where a beneficiary can also be the trustee. An example of this would be a disabled person who is capable of handling his or her own financial affairs. They may need to protect assets they had before their disability started or in the case where they receive a financial settlement after having become disabled.

For a seriously mentally ill person who cannot take care of his or her own finances, a third-party Special Needs Trust is the appropriate type to establish. Additionally, caretakers need to decide if they should create an *irrevocable* Special Needs Trust inside of a Living Trust or a stand-alone *revocable* SNT. It is fine to have an irrevocable SNT, built inside a Living Trust if you are 100% sure the beneficiary will not need a Special Needs Trust funded until the Trustee of the Living Trust passes away. However, if there is any chance that a disabled person will need to have their SNT funded while the Trustee(s) are alive, a separate stand-alone revocable SNT should be established.

Recommended Reading

The following recommended resources are broken down into categories. There is an obvious and unavoidable overlap in these categories.

Books Related to Current Mental Health Policy in the U.S.

Insane Consequences: How the Mental Health Care System Fails the Mentally Ill by DJ Jaffe
This is a comprehensive referendum on the broken mental health care system and how to fix it. I also recommend his website, www.MentalIllnessPolicy.org

Books Related to the History of the Mental Health Care Industry and Schizophrenia in Particular

Surviving Schizophrenia: A Manual for Families, Consumers, and Providers by Dr. E. Fuller Torrey
Comprehensive discourse on what is schizophrenia, how it has been treated in the last couple centuries and the modern day prognosis for this brain illness.

American Psychosis: How the Federal Government Destroyed the Mental Illness Treatment System by Dr. E. Fuller Torrey
Gives the reader an excellent understanding of American history of Mental Health Care and why it's not working in current times. Dr. Torrey is also the founder of www.TreatmentAdvocacyCenter.org

Books By Experts Dispensing Practical Advice and Resources

When Your Adult Child Breaks Your Heart by Joel Young, M.D. with Christine Adamec. Discusses the struggles a parent typically faces when trying to help their mentally ill son or daughter.

I Am Not Sick, I Don't Need Help by Dr. Xavier Amador This book provides tools for effective communication, garnering trust and de-escalating tensions, especially with a person who has no insight into their illness. This book is heavily promoted, rightly so, in NAMI Family Support meetings because it trains the reader in using much more effective communication skills. Search YouTube videos of Dr. Amador's LEAP method from *I Am Not Sick, I Don't Need Help*

The Everything Health Guide to Schizophrenia by Dean A. Haycock, Ph.D. The book's strength is that it covers a lot of topics.

Special Needs Trusts: Protect Your Child's Financial Future by Kevin Urbatsch. Not everyone has current assets they can leave their disabled child. But some parents get a Life Insurance Policy that will fund a Special Needs Trust for their loved one. If you do have assets they will inherit, a Special Needs Trust is essential.

When Someone You Love Has a Mental Illness by Rebecca Woolis, M.F.C.C. This is another practical guide in how to support the person in your life with serious mental illness, as well as their caretakers.

Days of Healing-Days of Joy: Daily Meditations for Adult Children by Earnie Larsen and Carol Larsen Hegarty
This inspirational guide has a quote and passage for each day of the year. "Adult children" refers to adult children of alcoholics, but this little book can be nurturing for anyone dealing with a loved one that has mental illness as well. I have found that each passage speaks to me directly, as well as issues I know my loved ones have experienced, helping me be more patient and compassionate.

Books Written By and For Mental Health Care Providers and Family Members

Breakdown: A Clinician's Experience in a Broken System of Emergency Psychiatry By Lynn Nanos, L.I.C.S.W. As a full-time mobile emergency psychiatric social worker, this is a candid account of her professional experience in getting psychotic people hospitalized and what happens after they are discharged.

Beyond Schizophrenia: Living and Working with a Serious Mental Illness by Marjorie L. Baldwin
This book covers a lot of issues, including the employment options for those with serious mental illness.

Recovery from Disability: Manual of Psychiatric Rehabilitation by Robert P. Liberman, M.D.
This book is a wealth of information and practical advice for all caretakers, family members, and professional mental

health care providers, from Dr. Liberman's extensive experience working with patients for decades.

Clozapine: *Meaningful Recovery From Schizophrenia* by Robert S. Laitman, M.D., Lewis Opler, M.D., Ph.D., Ann Mandel Laitman, M.D., Daniel Laitman, B.A. The book is written in four parts by each person. Dr. Laitman works with clients who have schizophrenia and he uniquely fine tunes the dosage of clozapine with other supplements to counter common side effects.

Mental Illness Memoirs

Crazy: *A Father's Search Through America's Mental Health Madness* by Pete Earley Former reporter for *The Washington Post* and well-known author, Pete Earley investigated the deplorable conditions for the mentally ill incarcerated in the Miami-Dade County prison system, while worried about his own mentally ill son's fate and legal problems.

Shot in the Head*: A Sister's Memoir, a Brother's Struggle* by Katherine Flannery Dering A very moving account of what she and her entire family of ten children went through in trying to support their brother with schizophrenia.

Behind the Wall: *The True Story of Mental Illness as Told By Parents* by Mary and Elin Widdifield, MA This book is a group effort, a collection of interviews of parents and their reactions to their family member with mental illness.

The Center Cannot Hold by Dr. Elyn R. Saks
This is USC Law professor, Elyn Saks' personal account of living with schizophrenia, starting when her illness emerged.

The Quiet Room: *A Journey Out of the Torment of Madness* by Lori Schiller & Amanda Bennett. This is a personal account by an articulate woman who gives us the experience of her own mental illness.

Search Youtube for "***Shattered Families***" (50 min.) Produced by Dr. Stephen Seager. I have watched this documentary at least five times as there is so much information in it.

Websites:

www.Schizophrenia.com

www.TreatmentAdvocacyCenter.org

www.MentalIllnessPolicy.org

DJ Jaffe passed away on August 23, 2020. He was one of the most well-known and respected Mental Illness Advocates. I hope that his website, www.MentalIllnessPolicy.org stays on-line and continues to be managed by his associates. It is a treasure trove of information and resources.

www.SpecialNeedsTrustAlliance.com

www.Nami.org

(Local NAMI chapters have their own websites as well.)

www.nationalshatteringsilencecoaltion.org

Please join this group, The National Shattering Silence
Coalition. They need more members and they have
many goals which serve all our interests to change
the laws and better the lives of our ill loved ones.

Acknowledgements

I'd like to acknowledge Lynn, Kathy and Carol for your continuous support and friendship. During my darkest hours, I know I was not fun to be around; thank you for listening.

I'd like to acknowledge all my NAMI-Mom friends, such as Ellie, Diana G., Judy, Diana R., Shelley, Debbi, Pat, Barbara, Sherri, and many more who have all joined forces to support each other as an extended family.

Thank you Gail Evanguelidi and Jim Farell for your support and selfless service, teaching people about conservatorships and Special Needs Trusts.

Thank you to those who not only read the first draft, but provided constructive feedback, such as Lynn Nanos, Dr. Laitman and Dr. Liberman.

I need to thank Mindy and the whole staff for treating me and my son like family, and more.

I especially need to thank Beth Wareham for your enthusiasm and excellent editing skills, along with publishing partner Lisa Hagan for taking my project on and validating the vision fueling my memoir.

Author Biography

Kartar Diamond has a long established career as a classically trained
Feng Shui author, consultant, and teacher since 1992. Kartar has
worked with thousands of clients and students in the area of Chinese
metaphysics as well as having a background in yogic practices and
meditation. These mystical traditions continuously help Kartar cope
and gave her the resolve to have a spiritual perspective when her
only son was stricken with schizophrenia.

Accepting serious mental illness in the family is a profound
struggle, but dealing with the mental health care system is in
many ways more challenging. Like other parents, Kartar began
to advocate for improvements in mental health services, only to
discover a shocking amount of professional incompetence and
disregard for some of the most vulnerable members of our society.
The tragedy of serious mental illness is exacerbated in virtually
every family when the mental health care system fails to treat the
disease, protect the suffering person and ignores their caring loved
ones trying to assist.

Based in Southern California, Kartar volunteers as a family
member presenter for law enforcement's Crisis Intervention
Training programs, designed to give police and sheriffs the tools
they need to better serve the mentally ill. Kartar has also been an
active member within her local NAMI Family Support groups.
Shining a light on the broken mental health care system, Kartar
intends to use this memoir as a national advocacy tool, to improve
the lives of those living with schizophrenia, as well as their families.
She may be contacted through www.NoahsSchizophrenia.com

Made in the USA
Middletown, DE
25 May 2022

66211219R00124